Verbal
Reasoning
& Comprehension

The 11+
Practice Book

with Assessment Tests

For the CEM (Durham University) test

Ages
10-11

Practise • Prepare • Pass
Everything your child needs for 11+ success

How to use this Practice Book

This book is divided into two parts — themed question practice and assessment tests.
There are answers with detailed explanations in the pull-out answer book.

Themed question practice

- Each page has practice questions on a different theme. Use these pages to work out your child's strengths and the areas they find tricky.

- The questions get harder down each page.

Assessment tests

- The second half of the book contains eight assessment tests, each with a mix of question types from the first half of the book.

- If you want to give your child timed practice, give them a time limit of 30 minutes for each test, and ask them to work as quickly and carefully as they can.

- The tests get harder from 1-8, so don't be surprised if your child finds the later ones more tricky.

- Your child should aim for a mark of around 85% (58 questions correct) in each test. If they score less than this, use their results to work out the areas they need more practice on.

- If they haven't managed to finish the test in time, they need to work on increasing their speed, whereas if they have made a lot of mistakes, they need to work more carefully.

- Keep track of your child's scores using the progress chart on the inside back cover of the book.

- This book gives your child intensive practice of the Verbal Reasoning sections of the test. There will be other elements on the real 11+ test, such as Maths and Non-Verbal Reasoning.

- Although our question types are based on those set by CEM, we cannot guarantee that your child's actual 11+ exam will take the same format or contain the same question types as this book.

Published by CGP

Editors:
Claire Boulter, Anthony Muller, Holly Poynton, Julie Wakeling

Contributors:
Chloe Buckley, Christine Holt, Steve Martin, Alison Mott, Katy Servante

Reviewer:
Alison Griffin

With thanks to Rebecca Tate and Luke von Kotze for the proofreading.

With thanks to the moderators of ElevenPlusExams.co.uk for their input.

Please note that CGP is not associated with CEM or The University of Durham in any way. This book does not include any official questions and it is not endorsed by CEM or The University of Durham.

CEM, Centre for Evaluation and Monitoring, Durham University and *The University of Durham* are all trademarks of The University of Durham.

ISBN: 978 1 84762 163 4
Printed by Elanders Ltd, Newcastle upon Tyne
Clipart from Corel®

Based on the classic CGP style created by Richard Parsons.

CONTENTS

Plurals

Write the correct plural of the word in brackets. Look at this example:

The choir performed in several __churches__ (church).

1. My ___heros___ (hero) are my mum and dad because they are firefighters.

2. There are no ___wolves___ (wolf) living wild in England now.

3. The tribe has had three different ___chiefs___ (chief) in the last decade.

4. The local people campaigned to keep the county's ___libaries___ (library) open.

5. The removal man sighed as he saw the ___pianos___ (piano) he had to move.

6. Mickey detested eating ___tomatos___ (tomato), even on pizza!

7. The clumsy ___thiefthens___ (thief) were destined to get caught.

8. Santa's ___elfs___ (elf) were back in the workshop on Boxing Day.

9. Snow covered the ___rooves___ (roof) of the houses opposite.

/ 9

Write the correct plural of the word in brackets. Look at this example:

The cook put cheese in traps to catch the ___mice___ (mouse).

10. We stopped at several tropical _____ (oasis) on our walk.

11. The _____ (child) were delighted with the new go-kart.

12. The insect waved its long _____ (antenna).

13. Fillipe and Guy played a game that involved rolling several _____ (die).

14. Cerys went to the park very early in the morning to watch the _____ (deer).

15. There's me, my mum and my two sisters, so my dad is surrounded by _____ (woman).

16. When my brother cooked dinner, it was a long series of _____ (crisis).

17. "Hand over _____ (that) custard pies at once!" my mum said angrily.

18. Many _____ (moose) were grazing peacefully on the plain.

Hint: These words are irregular, so sometimes letters in the middle of the word will change.

/ 9

Homophones

Homophones

Choose the correct homophone from the brackets. Look at this example:

> Archie tied a strong ___knot___ (**knot** **not**) in the ship's rigging.

1. The farmer had to move his stubborn _____ (**heard** **herd**) of cows into the barn.

2. Tanay didn't know _____ (**whether** **weather**) to eat the chocolate cake or the jelly.

3. It's vital to have a good breakfast; eating a nutritious _____ (**cereal** **serial**) can help.

4. Rebecca flexed the strong _____ (**muscles** **mussels**) in her arms.

5. The tomato _____ (**source** **sauce**) was as thick as treacle.

6. The ice-cream van drove _____ (**past** **passed**) the waiting crowd.

7. The wild wind blew the weather _____ (**vain** **vane**) off the church roof.

8. The _____ (**soul** **sole**) of my shoe had a gaping hole in it.

9. Queen Victoria _____ (**reigned** **reined**) for 63 years.

/ 9

Homophones

Underline the correct homophone to complete the sentence. Look at this example:

> The ticket will be in (**yore** **you're** <u>**your**</u>) wallet.

10. The boomerang landed in the shrubs over (**they're** **their** **there**).

11. If it's not (**to** **two** **too**) late, I'm going to come to the theatre.

12. Mika wanted to (**by** **buy** **bye**) a Christmas gift for his colleague.

13. Amy didn't have the faintest clue (**wear** **where** **ware**) she was going.

14. This wasn't the (**write** **rite** **right**) time to mention that the test had been postponed.

15. Asif was in (**ore** **oar** **awe**) of his older brother's new motorbike.

16. There was a long (**pours** **paws** **pause**) after the Prime Minister's speech.

17. (**By** **Buy** **Bye**) now for the lowest prices and best deals in town!

18. Matt was given a lot of (**prays** **preys** **praise**) for his volunteer work.

/ 9

Prefixes and Suffixes

Prefixes

Choose the correct prefix from the list to complete the word in each sentence: **un**, **in**, **pre**, **mis**, **re** or **dis**. Look at this example:

> Marcie felt very __un__ lucky because she never won anything.

1. I thought she was a coward, but I was __mis__ taken.
    un ?

2. The detective was _____ certain that the suspect was guilty.

3. Mum's carrot cake was simply ___un___edible!

4. I was lost, so I decided to ___pre___trace my steps. *re trace*
    not
    pre trace

5. It would be ___un___honest to say he had left the homework on the bus. *dishonest ?*

6. There have been many positive ___re___views of the new film.

7. Mrs Sajedi was ___un___capable of being bad-tempered around the children.

8. The burly men inside the car were obviously having a ___dis___agreement.

9. Make sure you ___re___heat the oven to the right temperature before you start.

Hint: Remember that 'pre' means 'before' and 're' means 'again'.

/ 9

Suffixes

Complete these sentences by adding a suffix to the word in brackets. Look at this example:

> That was such a __thoughtful__ **(thought)** present.

10. The __musician__ **(music)** took a deep breath as he took to the stage with his guitar.

11. The army sergeant demands loyalty, hard work and __tidiness__ **(tidy)** from his men.

12. I have fond memories from my __childhood__ **(child)** when I lived in the countryside.

13. Stacey wanted to avoid getting into an __argument__ **(argue)** about the missing book.

14. Many children around the world don't receive any __education__ **(educate)**.

15. Daneesh was very __hopeful__ **(hope)** that they would find his gerbil, Patches.

16. My brother has an __imaginative__ **(imagine)** friend called Brutus.

17. The stolen jewellery was precious and very __valuable__ **(value)**.

18. The elderly skydiver was a very __courageous__ **(courage)** man.

/ 9

Section One — Spelling and Grammar

Awkward Spellings

Vowels

Add either **ie** or **ei** to form the words correctly. Look at this example:

Jamie had a br _ie_ f wait at the station before his train arrived.

1. Abdul stood nervously on the stage as he waited to rec_ei_ve his prize.

2. The baubles dangling from the c_ei_ling were glittering in the lamp light.

3. Ian dec_ei_ved his dad by pretending to have done his homework.

4. When the spaceship landed in the garden, Peter knew he was having a really w_ei_rd day. *weird*

5. The businessman used the newspaper to sh_ie_ld himself from the rain.

6. Frankie could perc_ei_ve the distant sound of an ice-cream van.

7. My dad and my brother are both interested in books set in med_ie_val times.

8. Mrs DiFranco loves knitting and going swimming at the l_ei_sure centre. *leisure*

9. The policeman s_ei_zed the man by the arm and marched him to the police car. *seized*

/9

Consonants

Complete these words with the correct pair of consonants so that the sentence makes sense. Look at this example:

The cli _ff_ s by the sea looked very difficult to cli _mb_ .

10. Mina caught her thu_mb_ in the blades of the _sc_issors.

11. The chef cho_pp_ed the cabbage with a sharp _kn_ife.

Hint: Each letter pair is either a pair of double letters or has one silent letter.

12. The kitten's fur, which used to be flu_ff_y, was dri_pp_ing wet.

13. Grandma was busy _kn_itting a jumper for her li_tt_le grandson.

14. The hotel's acco_mm_odation was very expensive, so they ignored the vacancy si_gn_ .

15. Jimmy asked his mother if she would _wr_ite a note to excuse him from going swi_mm_ing.

16. When he jumped into the pu_dd_le, the water came up to his _kn_ees!

17. Andrea _gn_awed the end of her pencil as she tried to an_sw_er the question.

18. A colu_mn_ of black smoke ruined the beautiful mountain _sc_enery.

/9

Section One — Spelling and Grammar

Mixed Spelling Questions

Each sentence contains a spelling mistake. Underline the word with the error and write the correct spelling on the line. Look at this example:

Only three contestants <u>remaned</u> in the competition.   *remained*

1. The children were extreamly anxious about their voyage.   _____

2. Wolfgang strolled glumly along the corridor, feeling embarased.   _____

3. It was the forth time this week that James had missed a deadline.   _____

4. Marsha didn't enjoy going on long distence walks in the country.   _____

5. Simon knew that his football team were definately going to succeed.   _____

6. Mum's casserole was discusting; she wasn't the world's best chef.   _____

/ 6

Hint: Once you've identified the error, remember to write the correct spelling on the line.

7. Joe stuck on his fake moustache; it was the final piece of his disgise.   _____

8. Gustav tried to convinse the teacher not to give him a detention.   _____

9. My stomack aches because I've eaten far too much lasagne.   _____

10. The coach blew his whistle and expected an imediate response.   _____

11. The crowd erupted into applause, which deafend the actors on stage.   _____

12. Amy was alarmed by the shriek and glanced behind her hesitently.   _____

/ 6

13. The letters were privite, but Adam could not resist reading them.   _____

14. Once the seleccion box was opened, Sam rushed to grab a biscuit.   _____

15. Anya was desparate to win this year's school talent competition.   _____

16. I paid for my taxi but the driver was reluctant to give me a reciept.   _____

17. It was ridiculous how much the restaurant charged for desert.   _____

18. Gakuya arrived at the concert early so she was garanteed a seat.   _____

/ 6

Mixed Spelling Questions

Underline the correct word to complete each sentence. Look at this example:

The pens are in the **(stationary <u>stationery</u>)** cupboard.

1. Faizah likes to **(practise practice)** the piano every Wednesday afternoon.

2. Skateboarding is a skill that takes a lot of **(practise practice)**.

3. Closing the local shop will have a negative **(effect affect)** on the village.

4. Numerous factors can **(affect effect)** global climate change.

5. In America, a head teacher is called a **(principle principal)**.

6. Bijan turned down the job on **(principle principal)**.

/ 6

7. There are **(less fewer)** ducks on the pond than there were yesterday.

8. I have a lot **(less fewer)** money now that I've been on holiday.

9. Christine **(bought brought)** her flute to the orchestra recital.

10. Keisha **(bought brought)** the last pineapple in the entire market.

11. I was delighted when my sister **(past passed)** her driving test.

12. During the **(past passed)** year, I've saved enough money to buy a new camera.

/ 6

13. Agony Aunts often give their readers **(advice advise)** on relationships.

14. I would **(advice advise)** you to take off your socks before you paddle in the sea.

15. We **(accept except)** your apology, but please don't wake us up so early again.

16. Brianne adores all animals **(accept except)** snakes and lizards.

17. Professor Tate is trying to **(device devise)** a way of travelling through time.

18. My mobile phone is the only **(device devise)** I can't live without.

/ 6

Section One — Spelling and Grammar

Verbs

Underline the word or words in each sentence which match the part of speech in brackets. Look at this example:

> Paul hurried anxiously down the street. **(subject)**

1. The monk opened the ancient, rusty door. **(subject)**

2. The children giggled at the hamster scuttling about in his cage. **(subject)**

3. Mark and I viewed the gigantic drifts of snow outside. **(verb)**

4. Khalid and Marcus, the private detectives, resigned. **(verb)**

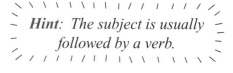

Hint: The subject is usually followed by a verb.

5. Outside the saloon, the outlaws defied the cruel sheriff. **(verb)**

6. Next summer my family are emigrating to France. **(subject)**

7. Mr Evans sighed as he gave Daniel's sister a new book. **(subject)**

8. Singing hurts my sore throat. **(subject)**

9. After a heavy snow fall, Sally's mum abandoned the car. **(verb)**

/ 9

Underline the correct verb from the brackets to complete each sentence. Look at this example:

> I **(is be <u>am</u>)** taking extra science classes.

10. When the hurricane was over, the boat **(sink sank sinks)** to the sea floor.

11. I **(were was am)** suffering last week, but I have improved since then.

12. **(Write Wrote Writing)** clearly so people can understand what you mean.

13. Leo reached the door, timidly raised his hand and **(rang rung ring)** the bell.

14. We **(continue continuing continues)** to be terribly anxious about yesterday's events.

15. I **(have am had)** just finished my dinner when I heard the shrill scream.

16. You **(will would have)** hear the result of the competition next week.

17. The gerbil had **(forgot forget forgotten)** where its tail was.

18. This morning I **(is am will)** be going to work in a spaceship.

/ 9

Verbs and Connectives

Verbs

Complete each sentence using the correct form of the verb in brackets. Write your answer on the line. Look at this example:

The rotten piece of cheese was ___stolen___ **(to steal)** by the mouse.

1. I ___spoke___ **(to speak)** in class, so the teacher shouted at me.

2. Pedro had never ___lended___ **(to lend)** me his favourite CD.

3. Who were you ___visited___ **(to visit)** yesterday?

4. Egbert says he will go to the zoo if Edwina ___came___ **(to come)** too.

5. Last month I ___did___ ___done___ **(to do)** an hour of exercise every day.

6. We were merrily on our way to Wales when we ___noticed___ **(to notice)** the deflated tyre.

7. When the boat capsized, the sailor ___swam___ **(to swim)** back to shore.

8. Mr Thomas ___threw___ **(to throw)** his socks in the washing machine yesterday.

9. He ___brung___ **(to bring)** crisps and lemonade to last summer's picnic.

Hint: Make sure the verb agrees with the subject and check that the tenses in each sentence agree.

/ 9

Connectives

Underline the most appropriate connective from the brackets to complete each sentence. Look at this example:

It has been six years **(when after <u>since</u>)** I saw that film.

10. I reached the crest of the hill **(because <u>before</u> if)** it started raining.

11. Sue would like to train to be a physician **(while <u>when</u> if)** she has left school.

12. Mike gobbled some chips **(unless despite <u>while</u>)** Ben was distracted.

13. I adore pasta **(<u>but</u> which if)** I am indifferent towards pizza.

14. The lights have been switched on **(although if <u>because</u>)** it is gloomy.

15. I will make Gran a delicious hot chocolate **(unless if furthermore)** she would prefer tea.

16. Ned works on Tuesdays **(despite <u>whereas</u> until)** Catelyn works on Fridays.

17. Dad had a broken leg; **(when <u>however</u> besides)**, he still went to work.

18. The sun was shining, **(<u>hence</u> despite whereas)** we packed some sun screen.

/ 9

Section One — Spelling and Grammar

Mixed Grammar Questions

Each sentence has one grammatical error. Underline the word which is wrong and write the correct word on the line. Look at this example:

Sarah and Kevin <u>is</u> getting married in June.   <u>are</u>

1. We must apologise because Louise ate all theirs lollipops.   _____

2. I were going to tell you the story when I arrived.   _____

3. The discontented children have wrote a long letter to their MP.   _____

4. The rusty car was advancing very slow towards the main road.   _____

5. I saw the cricketer throws the ball into the river.   _____

6. That ornamental rocking horse used to be my.   _____

7. What of these crayons shall I use for this drawing?   _____

8. We don't want no unnecessary noise from you.   _____

9. There is no available seats on this rickety bus.   _____

/9

Underline the word in each sentence which matches the part of speech in brackets. Look at this example:

Kieran <u>cleared</u> the table in a hurry. **(verb)**

10. Charlotte's school was in the centre of the city. **(proper noun)**

11. The fire was lit swiftly and the room felt warmer. **(adjective)**

12. The family of squirrels has its residence in the old oak tree. **(verb)**

13. The grey elephant sighed regretfully in the circus van. **(adverb)**

14. In the swimming pool, the children played contentedly. **(verb)**

15. Alice hurried nervously after the mouse. **(common noun)**

16. Theatres and cinemas are both popular in Paris. **(proper noun)**

17. The canary-yellow car drew up alongside the shops. **(adjective)**

18. The thief often hid the stolen jewels under his mattress. **(adverb)**

Hint: A proper noun starts with a capital letter and names things like people and places.

/9

Multiple Meanings

> Choose the word that has a similar meaning to the words in both sets of brackets. Underline your answer.
>
> Look at this example:
>
> (letters mail) (pole stake)   fence <u>post</u> parcel pillar

Hint: Cross out any words that you think are definitely wrong as you go along, e.g. pillar.

1. (dry clear)   (nice lovely)   bright good great fine

2. (turn revolve)   (bun bread)   snack spin circle roll

3. (pink blush)   (soared ascended)   red rose bloom floated

4. (take guide)   (first main)   command chief lead direct

5. (firm solid)   (difficult awkward)   rigid complex stiff hard

6. (error fault)   (muddle confuse)   wrong mistake puzzle baffle

/ 6

7. (near adjacent)   (shut secure)   lock adjoining close neighbouring

8. (article item)   (aim end)   object motive goal thing

9. (award medal)   (value cherish)   reward treasure love prize

10. (breeze gale)   (coil reel)   blow wind twist spiral

11. (rest recline)   (untruth deception) fake repose lounge lie

12. (bend curtsey)   (ribbon knot)   nod string bow stoop

/ 6

13. (grassland flatland) (simple obvious)   clear field distinct plain

14. (pit quarry)   (bomb explosive)   mine blast trench ditch

15. (precious beloved) (expensive costly)   overpriced cherished favourite dear

16. (shyness timidity) (book engage)   reserve modesty arrange organise

17. (use purpose)   (event party)   job function ball social

18. (reason basis)   (earth land)   soil ground theory field

/ 6

Closest Meaning

Find the word that means the same, or nearly the same, as the word on the left. Underline your answer.

Look at this example:

cup   bowl fork <u>mug</u> plate

1. **sizeable**   sturdy robust impressive immense

2. **honest**   truthful proper reliable loyal

3. **waste**   spend invest squander hoard

4. **devour**   swallowed greedy gobble nibble

5. **defeat**   seize attack oppose conquer

6. **stingy**   neglected miserly disowned poor

7. **depart**   leave embark vanish flee

Hint: If you don't recognise a word, look it up in the dictionary.

/ 7

8. **favourite**   approved preferred valuable populous

9. **gloomy**   dismal neglected shaded faint

10. **droop**   perish slump limp pucker

11. **pale**   blank fresh unsullied wan

12. **sneaky**   furtive eavesdrop unscrupulous ruthless

13. **strange**   infrequent ludicrous bizarre macabre

14. **rotten**   eroded perished putrid corroded

/ 7

15. **safe**   secure enclosed vulnerable confined

16. **memorable**   celebration nondescript noteworthy recollect

17. **childish**   energetic dependant juvenile demanding

18. **cunning**   malicious mischievous wily wicked

19. **grow**   breed develop teach nourish

20. **greedy**   gluttonous starving gorge plump

/ 6

Section Two — Word Meanings

Closest Meaning

Complete the word on the right so that it means the same, or nearly the same, as the word on the left.

Look at this example:

find [l][o][c][a][t][e]

1. **clippers** [s][ ][ ][ ][o][r][s]
2. **keen** [ ][ ][g][e][r]
3. **field** [ ][e][ ][d][ ][w]
4. **pedal** [c][ ][ ][l][e]
5. **legend** [m][ ][ ][h]
6. **fragment** [ ][c][ ][ ][p]
7. **optimistic** [p][o][ ][ ][ ][ ][v][e]

/ 7

8. **continue** [ ][ ][ ][c][e][e][d]
9. **teach** [t][ ][t][ ][r]
10. **giving** [g][ ][n][ ][ ][o][ ][ ]
11. **rain** [ ][r][i][ ][ ][l][e]
12. **scribble** [s][ ][r][ ][ ][l]
13. **impartial** [n][ ][ ][t][r][ ][l]
14. **stare** [ ][ ][z][ ]

Hint: Watch out for common suffixes like 'ing', 'ive' or 'ous'.

/ 7

15. **join** [ ][ ][i][t][e]
16. **sadness** [ ][r][i][e][ ]
17. **complete** [ ][n][t][ ][ ][e]
18. **twist** [ ][r][ ][n][g]
19. **flexible** [ ][ ][p][p][ ][ ]
20. **screech** [s][ ][ ][ ][w][k]

/ 6

Opposite Meaning

Find the word that means the opposite, or nearly the opposite, of the word on the left. Underline your answer.

Look at this example:

hot   angry cough <u>cold</u> shiver

1. **dull**   boring flat light bright

2. **fat**   small gaunt feeble flimsy

3. **ancient**   dirty elegant decorative modern

4. **nimble**   listless static awkward swift

5. **cease**   ban finish commence abolish

6. **serene**   busy frenzied slow troublesome

7. **accuse**   quarrel decide fight defend

Hint: If you're stuck, try looking in a thesaurus for words that mean the opposite — they're sometimes called 'antonyms'.

/ 7

8. **elderly**   infirm youthful inexperienced naive

9. **communal**   neighbour rural secluded separate

10. **improve**   deteriorate plateau halt reject

11. **genuine**   deficient bluff invalid counterfeit

12. **disagree**   equal argue concur permit

13. **misplace**   disappoint discover reveal provoke

14. **hopeful**   reluctant ashamed auspicious discouraged

/ 7

15. **crude**   restrained convenient serviceable refined

16. **clarify**   aghast uncertain disconcerted perplex

17. **talkative**   taciturn garrulous pensive unexpressive

18. **delighted**   sated mournful frustrated resentful

19. **constant**   overwhelming unexceptional fluctuating definitive

20. **easy**   onerous scintillating prolonged sustained

/ 6

Opposite Meaning

Complete the word on the right so that it means the opposite, or nearly the opposite, of the word on the left.

Look at this example:

above   b e l o w

1. **relaxed**   t ☐ ☐ s ☐ ☐
2. **clean**   f i ☐ ☐ h ☐
3. **release**   s ☐ ☐ z e
4. **pride**   s h ☐ ☐ ☐
5. **hot**   ☐ ☐ y
6. **cheap**   ☐ ☐ s ☐ l y
7. **order**   ☐ u d ☐ l ☐

/ 7

8. **reward**   p ☐ ☐ ☐ s h
9. **hidden**   ☐ ☐ p o s ☐ ☐
10. **worry**   ☐ e l ☐ e f
11. **freeze**   ☐ ☐ ☐ w
12. **plain**   ☐ r n a ☐ e
13. **safe**   ☐ ☐ s k ☐
14. **smooth**   j ☐ ☐ g e ☐

/ 7

15. **ally**   ☐ ☐ v ☐ l
16. **love**   l o ☐ t ☐ ☐
17. **delighted**   a p ☐ ☐ ☐ l e d
18. **crooked**   ☐ t r ☐ ☐ h t
19. **lose**   ☐ r i u m ☐ ☐
20. **decline**   t ☐ r ☐ v ☐

Hint: Make sure you check the spelling of your answer carefully — it's easy to muddle up letters when you're not writing the whole word out.

/ 6

Section Two — Word Meanings

Odd One Out

Three of the words in each list are linked. Underline the word that is not related to these three.

Look at this example:

dog   cat   gerbil   <u>badger</u>

Hint: Read all the words several times to make sure you understand them properly.

1. hammer   scissors   spanner   screwdriver

2. iron   lead   tin   gold

3. upset   angry   irate   cross

4. cushion   pillow   tarpaulin   rug

5. skirt   shirt   shorts   trousers

6. sock   boot   clog   sandal

7. scramble   muddle   chaotic   jumble

/ 7

8. elderly   tumbledown   ruined   crumbling

9. tough   hard   nasty   difficult

10. German   American   French   Italian

11. soothe   placate   calm   suppress

12. organize   combine   blend   mix

13. gripe   moan   grumble   fret

14. breach   trespass   invade   intrude

/ 7

15. pick   allow   choose   select

16. absurd   foolish   hilarious   ridiculous

17. chase   search   hunt   seek

18. parched   barren   arid   sweltering

19. hesitant   shy   wary   tentative

20. successful   ambitious   aspiring   hopeful

/ 6

Section Two — Word Meanings

Reorder Words to Make a Sentence

Rearrange the words so that each sentence makes sense.
Underline the word which doesn't fit into the sentence.

Look at this example:

it for time was <u>late</u> bed

The remaining words can be arranged into the sentence:
It was time for bed.

1. was dirty very and sewer the in it

2. cinema the a gave film horror me nightmare

3. I to be polishing my repaired shoes took

4. summer was a hot day in it sun

5. Greg the to weapon the in tomorrow handed police

6. disco loud music in had flashing the and lights

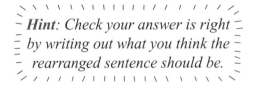

Hint: Check your answer is right by writing out what you think the rearranged sentence should be.

/ 6

7. the man down empty street walked old lights the

8. is rainbow to a see sight a weather beautiful

9. my then hair it shower and dried I washed

10. went it to pleasant is in the amble countryside

11. enjoy after meal of a cup I coffee food a

12. must mug you to tea order water in make boil

/ 6

13. learning lesson been since six was James has piano the he

14. angry naughty very was teacher child the with shouted the

15. enjoyed through watching the butterfly I look the air flutter

16. the pilot landed plane damaged adventure successfully the experienced

17. care mixture the when the into putting spoon oven cake take

18. put man's the cast injury plaster broken the leg a on doctor

/ 6

Section Two — Word Meanings

Using Rules of English

> Underline the most appropriate word from the brackets to complete each sentence. For example:
>
> Jonathan **(is am be are)** going to the match tomorrow.

Hint: Say the sentence out loud to help you work out the missing word.

1. I am not allowed out **(although when because why)** I returned home late last night.

2. Rob was playing the **(worse worst awful badly)** game of rugby of his whole career.

3. The baby had **(waked wakes woke woken)** up early and was gurgling quietly.

4. Dan ran ten miles **(because despite yet thus)** the very high temperature.

5. He had **(spoke spoken speak told)** to them about road safety.

6. We told him that the football stickers were **(our ours we us)**.

/ 6

7. Bob and his cousin **(likes likely enjoy like)** to go cycling in all conditions.

8. As he **(shake shook shaken shaked)** the groundsheet, a tiny spider sprang out.

9. **(Although Yet But Where)** the man was in agony, he limped to the hospital.

10. Raj **(cut cuts cutted cutting)** his glossy, curly hair when his mother was distracted.

11. There is a warning for all drivers to drive **(safe careful carefully quick)**.

12. I discovered the pencil **(what when which where)** I had mislaid.

/ 6

13. I would like to introduce you to my friend who **(going gone went go)** to Norway.

14. **(Therefore When But Moreover)** the puppy could not go outside, it became quite lethargic.

15. Davinda did not admit that she solved all of the equations **(easy easiest easily easiness)**.

16. Angus realised that he had **(broke broken break breaked)** his mother's priceless vase.

17. Emily **(brought bought buy buying)** her ticket from the conductor.

18. Marcus should **(have off had of)** washed the dog yesterday.

/ 6

Choose a Word

Choose the correct words to complete each passage below.

Cooking is not only a
1. ☐ costly
☐ useful
☐ bizarre
skill, it can also be great fun. Whether your passion
2. ☐ are
☐ was
☐ is

for beef stew or chocolate cake, there's
3. ☐ something
☐ nothing
☐ others
quite like the
4. ☐ satisfaction
☐ penance
☐ anxiety
of seeing

your family enjoying food that you have
5. ☐ completed
☐ eaten
☐ created
from scratch.

/ 5

King Arthur is a legendary warrior, who is
6. ☐ imagined
☐ hoped
☐ believed
to have lived around fifteen hundred years

7. ☐ ago
☐ past
☐ hence
. There are
8. ☐ frequent
☐ countless
☐ unusual
tales of Arthur's bravery and nobility,
9. ☐ including
☐ includes
☐ included
his

quest to find the Holy Grail,
10. ☐ and
☐ but
☐ so
nothing is known for certain.

/ 5

For as long as humans have
11. ☐ run
☐ walked
☐ ruined
the earth, they have been
12. ☐ intrigued
☐ fatigued
☐ wondered
by flight.

Attempts to fly date
13. ☐ from
☐ back
☐ to
more than a thousand years. In 1010 a Wiltshire monk built a glider

that he
14. ☐ flied
☐ flying
☐ flew
for about 200 metres,
15. ☐ after
☐ before
☐ upon
crashing and breaking both legs.

/ 5

Choose a Word

Choose the correct words to complete each passage below.

Children in Victorian Britain had

1. ☐ few
   ☐ fewer
   ☐ less
   ☐ least

toys than children

2. ☐ forthcoming
   ☐ earlier
   ☐ presently
   ☐ nowadays

. Whilst

rich children

3. ☐ often
   ☐ always
   ☐ never
   ☐ each

had rocking horses, toy soldiers and dolls made of wax or china, poor

children couldn't afford such

4. ☐ distractions
   ☐ luxuries
   ☐ results
   ☐ necessities

. They found

5. ☐ extra
   ☐ dangerous
   ☐ ingenious
   ☐ illegal

ways of making the

toys they wanted, such as creating dolls

6. ☐ for
   ☐ on
   ☐ out
   ☐ from

clothes pegs and balls out of old rags.

/ 6

I was

7. ☐ prepared
   ☐ dashing
   ☐ able
   ☐ eager

to start my holiday, so I didn't

8. ☐ envy
   ☐ begrudge
   ☐ forbid
   ☐ covet

getting up at the

crack of dawn to get to the airport. My

9. ☐ kindness
   ☐ patience
   ☐ diligence
   ☐ behaviour

began to wear a little thin when

the flight was

10. ☐ late
    ☐ behind
    ☐ delayed
    ☐ away

for four hours

11. ☐ because
    ☐ although
    ☐ whether
    ☐ albeit

the pilot couldn't be found,

but it was once

12. ☐ us
    ☐ they
    ☐ we
    ☐ you

boarded the plane that the fun really started.

/ 6

Section Three — Completing Passages

Fill in Missing Letters

Fill in the missing letters to complete the words in the following passages.

1. Ebenezer Scrooge is a bad-tempered miser who, des☐☐☐e being very rich,
2. refuses to help the p☐☐r and treats his loyal clerk, Bob Cratchit, very badly.
3. On Christmas Eve, Scrooge is visited by the ghost of his fo☐☐☐r business
4. partner Jacob Marley, who warns Scrooge that he must c☐☐nge his ways or
5. face an eternity of torment. Scrooge is then vi☐i☐☐d by the Ghost
6. of Christmas Past, who shows him how i☐☐oc☐nt he was as a boy,
7. and how he ☐eca☐e so cold-hearted.

/ 7

8. In Greek my☐☐☐logy , the baby Achilles was dipped in the River Styx by his
9. mo☐☐☐r , who hoped to make him immortal. However, because she held him
10. by his heel, this part of his body was not immersed, and remained mor☐☐☐ .
11. As an adult, Achilles gained a re☐☐☐ation as a mighty warrior who nobody
12. could defeat. One day, however, during an at☐☐☐k on the city of Troy,
13. Achilles was shot in the heel with an arrow, and k☐l☐ed . Even now,
14. a person's we☐☐☐ess is sometimes known as their 'Achilles heel'.

/ 7

15. Kingsley had always been a so☐i☐☐ry child, prone to daydreaming. His best
16. f☐☐☐nd was his dog, Tyke, who went everywhere with him. One day during the
17. summer holidays, Kingsley and Tyke set off early to e☐p☐☐re the ruined castle
18. that squatted on the hill, looming over the v☐☐☐age like a dark cloud. As
19. Kingsley trud☐☐☐ up the hill, Tyke scampered ahead of him, barking joyfully
20. and c☐☐s☐ng imaginary rabbits. As soon as the castle's shadow
21. fell on Tyke, however, his happy barks changed to whines of un☐☐se .

/ 7

Fill in Missing Letters

Fill in the missing letters to complete the words in the following passages.

1. When you mention dinosaurs, most people t◻◻◻k of giants like the lumbering

2. Brontosaurus or fer◻c◻◻us Tyrannosaurus rex, but in fact many dinosaurs were

3. tiny. One of the s◻◻◻◻est dinosaurs was the Lesothosaurus, which lived in

4. southern Africa about two hundred million years ago, and was ro◻◻◻ly the

5. same size as a chic◻◻◻ . It walked on two legs, and its long hind legs and long

6. tail s◻◻◻est that it was a fast runner. From fossils of its teeth,

7. s◻◻◻n◻ists can tell that the Lesothosaurus fed on plants.

/7

8. Standing on the b◻◻◻ony outside her room, Carla closed her eyes and let

9. the warm sun wash over her face. The gentle br◻◻◻e brought the fresh,

10. in◻◻◻◻rating scent of salt and the distant cries of children splashing

11. happily in the warm ocean. Carla and her mum had just ar◻◻◻ed for a

12. two-week stay with her mum's oldest friend, exchan◻◻◻◻ the cold Glasgow

13. winter for some Italian sun. As she p◻ct◻◻ed the weeks to come,

14. Carla sighed happily, k◻◻◻ing it would be the best holiday ever.

/7

15. On the 24th August AD 79, Mount Vesuvius in Italy e◻◻◻ted catastrophically,

16. burying the town of Pompeii u◻◻◻r many metres of ash. The residents were

17. completely unprepared for the d◻◻as◻◻r, and while some tried to flee the

18. town, others took shelter in their homes or in ◻◻◻lic buildings. All who stayed

19. were killed by the immense heat or su◻◻◻◻ating ash, and their remains were

20. buried and p◻◻◻erved . Today, Pompeii is an important site for

21. archaeologists, providing a un◻◻◻e perspective on Roman life.

/7

Finding Hidden Facts

> Read the information carefully, then use it to answer the question that follows. Write your answer on the line.

Hint: Using a tally chart for each question can help you keep track of the information.

1. John, Eleanor, Claire, Reuben and Mallika all take part in different sports.

   Claire, Reuben and Mallika all go trampolining. Everyone except Claire likes to play basketball. No-one except John plays hockey. John, Eleanor and Claire all take part in athletics. Eleanor is the only one who does not play cricket.

   Who takes part in the **fewest** sports? _____

2. Pavel, Luke, Maddie, Rosie and William are discussing the things they collect.

   William and Rosie both collect badges. Everyone except Rosie collects stamps. Maddie collects badges and postcards. The only one who collects stickers is Luke. Only two children, Pavel and Luke, collect marbles.

   Who collects the **fewest** things? _____

3. Joel, Trudi, Eli, Sacha and Leo are at a pizza party.

   Joel, Eli and Sacha each have one slice of cheese and tomato pizza. Leo and Joel both take a slice of ham and pineapple pizza. Everyone except Leo has a slice of pepperoni pizza. Sacha is the only child who takes a slice of chicken and mushroom pizza. The only one not to have a slice of roast vegetable pizza is Joel.

   Who takes the **most** slices of pizza? _____

4. Anna, Hayley, Michael, Helen and Simon go to a snack bar together.

   Anna, Hayley and Simon all choose burgers. Everyone has a portion of chips except Michael. Helen has a hot dog and a salad. Simon has a burger and chips. Michael is the only child who chooses a toasted sandwich.

   Which child orders the **most** items? _____

/ 4

Understanding the Language in the Text

Read the passage below, then answer the questions that follow.
Underline the correct option for each question.

1   "You've missed again," the soldier muttered, as the grappling hook just missed its target.

2   Hearing the angry shouts in the distance, he was reminded just how important this mission was.

3   He looked up at the cruel watchtower nearby.

4   "Well, I'll just have to try again, won't I?" the other man said, as he took aim once more.

5   "After all, everyone knows that that's where the prisoner is being held. All I have to do is climb

6   over that mile-high wall, overpower a few hundred guards, break through a steel door and

7   rescue him. Easy!"

8   The second grappling hook shot through the dark night sky like a rocket,

9   and clanged against the top of the wall.

10   "Who's there?" The snarling voice was a dagger ripping through the silence of the night.

Hint: Read all three options before you decide which one to underline.

1.   The author says that the soldier "muttered" (line 1). What impression does this give you of the soldier?
     A He's annoyed.   **B** He's tired.   **C** He's shy.

2.   The author compares the grappling hook to a "rocket" (line 8). What does this tell you about
     the grappling hook?
     A It is dangerous.   **B** It moves quickly.   **C** It makes a banging noise.

3.   The hook "clanged" (line 9) against the wall. What effect does this word have on the reader?
     A It shocks the reader.   **B** It makes the story scary.   **C** It helps you imagine the noise.

4.   The voice is described as a "dagger" (line 10). This shows that the speaker is:
     A dangerous.   **B** strong.   **C** brave.

5.   The man says that he needs to climb over "that mile-high wall" (line 6). Why does he say this?
     A He's exaggerating.   **B** He's intimidated.   **C** He can't see very well.

6.   Why does the man say that his task will be "Easy" (line 7)?
     A He's being practical.   **B** He's being optimistic.   **C** He's being ironic.

/ 6

Multiple-Statement Questions — Logic

Read the information carefully, then use it to answer the question that follows. Underline the correct answer.

Hint: Read each question several times before you try to answer it.

1. April, Sandy, Hamish, Drew and Kai are comparing their marks from a maths test.

   Kai didn't come last. Sandy got more right than April. April came third. Hamish got the most right.

   Which one of the sentences below **cannot** be true?

       A April only took 15 minutes to finish the test.

       B Kai got fewer marks than April.

       C Drew came fourth.

       D April got more right than Drew.

2. Aneequa, Carly, Sophie, Orla and Tim each toss a coin three times.

   Aneequa tosses a tail and two heads. Orla tosses three tails. Tim tosses two tails and a head. Sophie tosses heads each time.

   Which one of the sentences below **cannot** be true?

       A More tails were tossed than heads.

       B Carly tossed all heads.

       C An equal number of heads and tails were tossed.

       D Tim won the coin toss.

3. Rich, Tom, Wanda, Sam and Amir all take part in sailing race.

   Tom didn't finish last. Amir finished before Rich. Wanda finished after Sam. Rich came second.

   Which one of the sentences below **must** be true?

       A Rich came third.

       B Tom came fourth.

       C Amir came second.

       D Wanda finished last.

/ 3

Mixed Comprehension Questions

Read the passage below, then answer the questions that follow.

According to ancient Greek legend, the King of the Gods was the all-powerful Zeus. He had a daughter, Persephone, whose mother was Demeter, goddess of the crops and harvest. Persephone was a dutiful daughter and was deeply loved by her parents. One day, however, she left Demeter's side to go and collect wild flowers. When Persephone didn't return, Demeter

5   was distraught and wandered the Earth searching for her missing daughter.

Demeter decided to ask the Sun where Persephone had gone; it travelled across the sky each day so was sure to have seen what had happened. The Sun informed Demeter that he had seen Persephone collecting flowers when a chasm had opened in the Earth and she had been abducted by Hades, Lord of the Underworld.

10   Hades was besotted with Persephone and had taken her into his dark realm to be his bride. The Underworld was a cold, shadowy kingdom where the stern and pitiless Hades judged the souls of those who died and punished those he found to be wicked.

Frantically, Demeter implored Zeus to rescue Persephone. However, the King of the Gods refused to intervene. Demeter longed for her daughter to return and she quickly lost interest in

15   her duties as goddess of the crops and harvest. The fruit and vegetables on the Earth withered and died and, with no crops to harvest, the world suffered a terrible famine. When the starving human race begged Zeus for help, he finally relented and forcefully ordered Hades to release Persephone.

Hades was neither strong nor courageous enough to defy Zeus, but the shrewd Hades was

20   not going to free Persephone so easily. He knew of an unbreakable rule which stated that whoever ate or drank in the Underworld could never completely escape. So, before releasing her, Hades tricked the unfortunate Persephone into eating a single, tiny pomegranate seed. Once she had done this, Persephone was unable to leave the Underworld permanently and had to spend one third of each year there.

25   When mother and daughter were reunited, the Earth burst into life. Crops grew and the vines and trees were heavy with fruit. However, every year the time came for Persephone to return to Hades for four months. During this time, Demeter grew unhappy and refused to let the crops grow until Persephone returned. When Demeter was reunited with her daughter, the crops started to grow and the people of the Earth knew that winter was over and spring had

30   begun.

Mixed Comprehension Questions

Answer these questions about the text.
Circle the letter of the correct option for each question.

1. Why did Hades abduct Persephone?

   A   He wanted the human population to starve.

   B   He was in love with Persephone.

   C   He wanted to be King of the Greek Gods.

   D   He wanted to judge Persephone's soul.

2. Demeter behaved "Frantically" (line 13) because:

   A   the human population was starving.

   B   she had lost interest in her duties as goddess of the crops.

   C   she was upset that Hades had abducted Persephone.

   D   she did not want Hades and Persephone to get married.

3. Why did the crops on Earth die?

   A   Hades was punishing the human race for being wicked.

   B   Hades took them into the Underworld to feed to Persephone.

   C   The human race had eaten the crops because they were starving.

   D   Demeter was too upset to care about the crops.

4. Why did Zeus finally order Hades to release Persephone?

   A   Persephone was his daughter.

   B   People pleaded with him for help.

   C   Demeter was unhappy.

   D   He was angry with Hades.

5. What happened when Persephone returned from the Underworld?

   A   She left Demeter to collect wild flowers.

   B   The crops started to grow again.

   C   She could only spend four months with Demeter every year.

   D   She was forced to eat a pomegranate seed.

/ 5

Turn over for the next question

Mixed Comprehension Questions

Answer these questions about the text on page 26.
Circle the letter of the correct option for each question.

6. Why do you think Hades is described as "shrewd" (line 19)?

   A   He wanted to marry Persephone.

   B   He tricked Persephone.

   C   He didn't want to let Persephone go.

   D   He didn't want to make Zeus angry.

7. According to the passage, which statement about Hades is not true?

   A   He was frightened of Zeus.

   B   He killed wicked people.

   C   He was in love.

   D   He punished people.

8. What does this legend help to explain?

   A   Why there are famines

   B   Why the Underworld exists

   C   Why winter occurs

   D   Why pomegranate seeds are poisonous

9. What does the word "abducted" (line 9) mean?

   A   Stolen

   B   Kidnapped

   C   Harmed

   D   Attacked

10. What does the word "implored" (line 13) mean?

   A   Begged

   B   Suggested

   C   Required

   D   Convinced

/ 5

Assessment Test 1

The rest of this book contains eight assessment tests, which get progressively harder.

Allow 30 minutes to do each test and work as quickly and as carefully as you can.

You can print **multiple-choice answer sheets** for these questions from our website — go to www.cgplearning.co.uk/11+. If you'd prefer to answer them in standard write-in format, just follow the instructions in the question.

> Read this passage carefully and answer the questions that follow.

The First Day

Daniel felt as if he was being swallowed alive as he walked down the rowdy corridor and squinted through the thick lenses of his spectacles at the school hall beyond. The corridor was like the throat of a terrifying beast and he was sliding down it into the big belly that was the school hall.

He knew what would happen when he got there. All the new pupils, like himself, would be sitting
5   in rows waiting for the headmaster to make his welcome address. The headmaster at St Joseph's was a towering, severe man who could strike fear into any pupil. He was not a man who would put up with any nonsense whatsoever. Daniel knew this. He knew it because when Mr Graham was not busy being the headmaster, he was busy being Daniel's dad. Now, of course, his dad would be able to do both simultaneously and Daniel was sure that he would never hear the end of it from his classmates. He felt
10 thoroughly miserable; he was never going to make any friends.

"Hello," a voice said behind him. "You must be new too. My name's Rachael."

The girl was stunning. She thrust her hand out confidently towards Daniel, while he gaped at her.

"Dennis!" he blurted, finally shaking her hand, "I mean... Daniel. My name's Daniel."

"Don't you know your own name?" Rachael laughed. She didn't seem to be nervous at all.

15 "You're the head teacher's son, aren't you? Everyone says he's intimidating but my brother Tom, who's in the year above us, says that his bark is worse than his bite. It'll be weird for you, calling your dad 'Sir', won't it?"

"Yeah, I suppose," Daniel mumbled. He couldn't believe his luck: Rachael wanted to be his friend. Daniel thought secondary school might not be so bad after all.

> Answer these questions about the text that you've just read.
> Circle the letter of the correct answer.

1.   Which word best describes how Daniel feels at the start of the passage?

A   Anxious
B   Excited
C   Unlucky
D   Angry

2.   Which of these statements is true?

A   There is a beast in the school hall.
B   Daniel cannot see the school hall.
C   There are no other children in the corridor.
D   Daniel wears glasses.

/ 2

Carry on to the next question → →

3. Which word best describes what Daniel's father looks like?

A Bald
B Tall
C Thin
D Broad

4. Daniel tells Rachael that his name is Dennis at first. Why do you think he does this?

A She approached him from behind so he was surprised.
B He doesn't want to be Rachael's friend.
C He was nervous because she was so pretty.
D He did not like being called Daniel.

5. How does Daniel think the other pupils will treat him?

A They will be unkind and unfriendly.
B They will be nervous but welcoming.
C They will be kind and friendly.
D They won't know what to say to him.

6. How do you think Rachael's brother Tom knows what the headmaster is like?

A Tom is a friend of Daniel's.
B He has heard what the headmaster is like.
C The headmaster knows Tom's parents.
D He already goes to the school.

7. How do you think Daniel feels at the end of the passage?

A Miserable
B Relieved
C Shocked
D Uncomfortable

8. Which of the following facts is given in the passage?

A Rachael's surname
B Daniel's age
C Daniel's surname
D The name of Daniel's new form tutor

/ 6

9. What is meant by the word "address" (line 5)?

A Directions to classes
B The place where someone lives
C A formal speech
D An official warning

10. What is meant by the word "severe" (line 6)?

A Strict
B Miserable
C Thin
D Unreasonable

11. What is meant by the word "simultaneously" (line 9)?

A One after the other
B In an effective way
C By sharing the tasks
D At the same time

12. Why do you think Rachael doesn't feel nervous about starting a new school?

A Because she has already met Daniel.
B Because she knows what to expect.
C Because she knows the headmaster.
D Because she found her old school boring.

13. Daniel thinks that he will "never hear the end of it" (line 9).
    What do you think this phrase means?

A His dad will punish him at home if he misbehaves in school.
B The other children will tease Daniel for being the headmaster's son.
C His dad will boast about being Daniel's headmaster.
D The other children will ignore Daniel because he's the headmaster's son.

14. Rachael says "his bark is worse than his bite" (line 16).
    What do you think this phrase means?

A The headmaster only punishes those who deserve it.
B The headmaster has a bad temper.
C The headmaster never punishes anyone.
D The headmaster is not as scary as he seems.

/ 6

Carry on to the next question → →

Assessment Test 1

> Fill in the missing letters to complete the words in the following passage.

15. Over four and a half thousand years ago, the `A` `n` `c` ☐ ☐ ☐ `t`

16. Egyptians began ☐ ☐ `i` `l` `d` ☐ `n` `g` pyramids.

17. The pharaohs `i` `n` ☐ ☐ ☐ `d` `e` `d` the pyramids to be

18. impressive monuments: eternal resting `p` `l` ☐ ☐ ☐ `s`

    to safeguard their souls.

19. Wealthy Egyptians would fill their tombs with the ☐ `h` ☐ ☐ `g` `s`

20. they would need in the afterlife, but they `b` `e` `l` ☐ ☐ ☐ `e` `d`

21. that before their souls were `g` `r` `a` ☐ ☐ ☐ `d` eternal life,

22. their `a` ☐ `t` ☐ ☐ `n` `s` on Earth would be judged rigorously.

23. This ☐ `u` `d` `g` `e` ☐ ☐ `n` `t` would happen in the underworld,

24. where the deceased person's heart would be `w` `e` ☐ ☐ `h` `e` `d`

    against the feather of the goddess Ma'at.

25. If the heart was `h` `e` `a` ☐ ☐ ☐ `r` than the feather,

26. it would be deemed `u` `n` `w` ☐ ☐ `t` `h` ☐ and the person

27. would not `e` `n` ☐ ☐ `r` the afterlife.

28. Djoser's Step Pyramid was one of the `f` ☐ ☐ ☐ `t` of these tombs.

29. It is known as a step pyramid `b` `e` ☐ ☐ ☐ `s` `e` it was built

30. as a series of six successively ☐ ☐ ☐ ☐ `l` `l` `e` `r` squares

31. on top of one `a` `n` `o` ☐ ☐ ☐ ☐ `r`.

32. The burial chamber is `h` `i` ☐ ☐ ☐ `n` underground

    and sealed with a stone weighing 3.5 tonnes,

33. but this did not `d` `e` ☐ ☐ ☐ `r` the grave robbers.

    When the tomb was excavated,

34. almost `n` ☐ ☐ `t` ☐ ☐ ☐ `g` was left inside.

/ 20

Mark the word outside the brackets that has a similar meaning to the words in both sets of brackets.

Example: (find discover)   (stain blemish)   freckle smudge <u>spot</u> see

35. (point direct)   (purpose intention)   goal aim motive guide

36. (trench drain)   (abandon dump)   drop gutter ditch leave

37. (talent ability)   (present offering)   gift bonus skill flair

38. (path route)   (hunt pursue)   way chase passage track

39. (law code)   (lead reign)   rule govern order instruct

40. (assess grade)   (scratch dent)   judge mark rate cut

41. (people tribe)   (run sprint)   dash nation race type

42. (late overdue)   (after following)   delayed next detained behind

43. (stone boulder)   (swing sway)   roll rock tilt cobble

44. (bolt fasten)   (ringlet curl)   hair seal plait lock

/ 10

Complete the word on the right so that it means the opposite, or nearly the opposite, of the word on the left.

Example: smooth   r o u g h

45. sweet   ☐ i ☐ t ☐ r

46. poor   ☐ e a l ☐ h ☐

47. dry   ☐ o ☐ s t

48. bright   s ☐ ☐ d y

49. temporary   ☐ e r m ☐ ☐ ☐ n t

50. slow   ☐ ☐ e e ☐ y

51. joy   w ☐ ☐

52. rare   ☐ ☐ o m ☐ ☐ n

53. uninterested   e ☐ ☐ g ☐ r

54. professional   a m a t ☐ ☐ ☐

/ 10

Carry on to the next question → →

Assessment Test 1

Find the word that means the same, or nearly the same, as the word on the left.

Example: small <u>tiny</u> strong large soft

55. **brave**   noble fearless capable tough

56. **guess**   consider estimate belief idea

57. **worth**   payment value expensive reward

58. **study**   teach student learn education

59. **assist**   treat remedy cure aid

60. **glad**   comforted pleased comical witty

61. **shovel**   excavate sift tunnel scoop

62. **ring**   around shape band tunnel

63. **bendy**   broken flexible snap springy

64. **tight**   taut solid immovable tense

65. **scare**   afraid shock frightful fluster

66. **shrink**   slight miniature wane simplify

67. **soak**   drench damp drip clean

68. **blunt**   curt silent secretive defensive

/ 14

Total   / 68

End of Test

Assessment Test 2

Allow 30 minutes to do this test and work as quickly and as carefully as you can.

You can print **multiple-choice answer sheets** for these questions from our website — go to www.cgplearning.co.uk/11+. If you'd prefer to answer them in standard write-in format, just follow the instructions in the question.

> Read this passage carefully and answer the questions that follow.

A Brave Step Forward

It was September, 1921. Eighteen-year-old Antonio and his friend Manolo were very excited; several weeks ago they had left their families on the island of Trinidad and had crossed the Atlantic Ocean in a small cargo ship carrying spices. The journey had been very arduous and Antonio would be glad to reach dry land; he had suffered from sea-sickness on the stormier days of the journey.

5 Now that they had nearly reached Plymouth, Antonio's thoughts turned to his departure from Trinidad all those weeks ago. His mother had hugged him goodbye at the port, and had whispered in his ear that she had promised herself she wouldn't cry because she aspired to be as strong and courageous as he was. But as he stood on the deck of the ship waving farewell to his family, he tasted salty tears in his mouth and he felt an ache in his chest.

10 Although leaving his family had been very difficult, Antonio thought that he had made the right decision. After several years of taking intensive examinations at school, Antonio and Manolo had been told that they were ready to train as doctors. Antonio's father, who was a doctor himself and had always hoped that at least one of his two children would follow in his footsteps, had advised them that the best place to undertake medical training was London, in one of the big teaching hospitals.

15 As the boat neared the dock, Antonio began to feel slightly apprehensive. He had never left Trinidad before and he had not been away from his parents for any substantial length of time. He thought of his mother and his younger sister, Rosa; they seemed a long way away. He knew he was arriving in Plymouth but he did not have an inkling of how to reach London from there, or where they would spend the night when they arrived. The closer they came to the dock, the more he felt the knots
20 in his stomach tighten. He had taken a huge step, but was it the right one?

> Answer these questions about the text that you've just read.
> Circle the letter of the correct answer.

1. Why didn't Antonio's mother cry when he left?

A   She didn't want Antonio to think she was weak.
B   She wanted to be as brave as Antonio.
C   She was proud that he was ambitious.
D   She was happy that he would be a doctor.

2. Why was Antonio glad that his journey was nearly over?

A   He was looking forward to seeing England.
B   He had found the journey long and he had been ill.
C   He wanted to visit London.
D   He wanted to start his medical training.

/ 2

Carry on to the next question → →

3. Which of the following is not mentioned in the text?

A Where the boys had come from.
B Which ocean they had sailed across.
C How old Manolo is.
D How Antonio feels about reaching England.

4. Where was Antonio's final destination?

A A hospital in London
B Plymouth
C Trinidad
D A hotel in London

5. How do you think Antonio's father felt about Antonio leaving home?

A Despondent
B Conceited
C Proud
D Jealous

6. Which of the following statements about the boys' journey is not true?

A The journey was stormy.
B The boys travelled on a large ship.
C The first stop on the journey was Plymouth.
D The ship carried passengers and cargo.

7. Which of the following statements is true?

A Antonio was the oldest child in his family.
B Antonio had a brother.
C Antonio's mother was a doctor.
D Antonio's mother was called Rosa.

8. Why do you think Antonio felt "an ache in his chest" (line 9)?

A His parents had sacrificed a lot so that he could go to England.
B He hadn't said goodbye to his father.
C He had lied to his mother about where he was going.
D He wasn't as brave as his mother thought he was.

/ 6

9.   The students took "intensive examinations" (line 11). This means that the examinations were:

A   important.
B   detailed.
C   expensive.
D   demanding.

10. What is meant by the word "apprehensive" (line 15)?

A   Frightened
B   Nervous
C   Excited
D   Upset

11. What is meant by the word "inkling" (line 18)?

A   The slightest hope
B   A set of accurate directions
C   A vague idea
D   Any chance at all

12. Which of the following statements is true?

A   Antonio failed his exams the first time he took them.
B   Antonio has never been abroad before.
C   Antonio has never spent a night away from home.
D   Manolo and Antonio are brothers.

13. Why did Antonio's father want him to go to England?

A   Because doctors are paid more in England than in Trinidad.
B   Because Antonio's father trained in England.
C   Because Antonio had family in England he could stay with.
D   So that he could get the best medical training possible.

14. Antonio's father hopes that at least one of his children will "follow in his footsteps" (line 13).
     What do you think this phrase means?

A   Take over his medical practice when he retires.
B   Choose the same career path that he did.
C   Stay at home and look after the family.
D   Make their own way in the world.

/ 6

Carry on to the next question → →

Circle the letters which correspond to the correct words to complete the passage below.

Freddie had a vivid imagination,
15. **A** however
B but
C so
D while
it was no surprise when he
16. **A** announced
B agreed
C thought
D guessed
that

he would be
17. **A** home
B early
C late
D hungry
for tea on Friday because he was
18. **A** go
B going
C went
D goes
on a school trip to a

distant galaxy. The trip was free as the alien pupils
19. **A** will
B was
C did
D were
providing the spaceship. He would

20. **A** require
B choose
C wish
D demand
a packed lunch and several changes of clothes as they would
21. **A** want
B be
C are
D like
travelling

22. **A** with
B for
C near
D by
centuries. Smirking, Mum
23. **A** offered
B preferred
C liked
D suggested
putting Astronaut Lollipops in his lunch box.

Dad joked
24. **A** away
B about
C with
D between
weighing down his trainers. Freddie just smiled that
25. **A** secretive
B furious
C sullen
D tedious
smile

he reserved for occasions when
26. **A** he
B them
C they
D nobody
clearly didn't
27. **A** like
B believe
C suffer
D doubt
him.

The next week, Mum
28. **A** moved
B paused
C yawned
D waited
patiently with the other parents. At six o'clock, there was a brief

shudder and a gentle
29. **A** whisper
B screech
C howl
D roar
of air, then forty excited children emerged out
30. **A** off
B of
C for
D with

nowhere
31. **A** accompanied
B abandoned
C united
D combined
by an identical number of bright blue aliens
32. **A** in
B of
C with
D have
enormous eyes.

"Didn't I mention,"
33. **A** ask
B asks
C asking
D asked
Freddie as Mum's
34. **A** jaw
B teeth
C eyes
D nose
dropped, "it's an exchange visit?"

/ 20

Fill in the missing letters to complete the words in the following passage.

35. Mr Sugar's sweet shop was [p][a][ ][ ][ ][d].

36. Every [s][h][ ][ ][ ] was laden with jars of bright bon-bons.

37. Children were [g][a][z][ ][ ][ ] at the smooth, golden toffees,

38. wrapped in gold paper, and the [e][x][ ][ ][i][ ][i][t][e]

    Swiss truffles in gilded boxes.

39. A barrel of [g][l][ ][ ][m][ ][ ][g] white mints stood by the

    door opposite a display of freshly baked gingerbread men.

40. There were crunchy honeycomb [p][i][ ][ ][ ][s] and

    gobstoppers the size of ping-pong balls.

41. Mr Sugar presided over it all in his striped [a][p][r][ ][ ],

42. doling out ice creams in every [f][ ][a][ ][ ][ ][r], from

    butterscotch to cherry cream, and mango to raspberry ripple.

/ 8

Find the word that means the opposite, or nearly the opposite, of the word on the left.

Example: **tame**   angry   <u>wild</u>   strong   calm

43. **sturdy**   dense frail light bulky

44. **link**   joint fragment detach exclude

45. **confident**   shy surly jealous brave

46. **wealthy**   modest needy pitiful sad

47. **early**   initial before previous delayed

48. **dangerous**   gallant risky secure careless

49. **join**   separate tangle saturate organise

50. **few**   robust many great colossal

/ 8

Carry on to the next question → →

Find the word that means the same, or nearly the same, as the word on the left.

Example: **small**   <u>tiny</u>   strong   large   soft

51. **mend**   heal   screw   staple   fix

52. **pretty**   dainty   precious   adorable   beautiful

53. **happy**   laughing   clapping   pleased   excited

54. **fall**   lunge   tumble   squash   leap

55. **clue**   hint   suspicion   guess   signal

56. **ruin**   collapsed   injure   spoil   wound

57. **shoot**   bullet   barrel   fire   target

58. **note**   list   message   essay   report

59. **under**   around   adjacent   behind   below

60. **lock**   protect   handcuff   bolt   arrest

61. **whisper**   articulate   murmur   hoarse   secretive

62. **easy**   calm   carefree   simple   sensible

/ 12

Complete the word on the right so that it means the opposite, or nearly the opposite, of the word on the left.

Example: smooth   [r][o][u][g][h]

63. shallow   [ ][ ][ ][p]

64. wide   [ ][a][ ][r][ ][w]

65. above   [ ][ ][e][a][ ][h]

66. raw   [ ][o][k][ ][d]

67. small   [ ][n][ ][r][m][ ][ ][s]

68. straight   [ ][u][ ][l][y]

/ 6

Total   / 68

End of Test

Assessment Test 3

Allow 30 minutes to do this test and work as quickly and as carefully as you can.

You can print **multiple-choice answer sheets** for these questions from our website —
go to www.cgplearning.co.uk/11+. If you'd prefer to answer them in standard write-in
format, just follow the instructions in the question.

> Read this passage carefully and answer the questions that follow.

An abridged extract from 'Jane Eyre'

Five o'clock had hardly struck on the morning of the 19th of January, when Bessie brought a
candle into my closet and found me already up and nearly dressed. I had risen half-an-hour before
her entrance, and had washed my face, and put on my clothes by the light of a half-moon just setting,
whose rays streamed through the narrow window near my crib.

5   I was to leave Gateshead that day by a coach which passed the lodge gates at six a.m. Bessie
was the only person yet risen; she had lit a fire in the nursery, where she now proceeded to make my
breakfast. Few children can eat when excited with the thoughts of a journey; nor could I. Bessie,
having pressed me in vain to take a few spoonfuls of the boiled milk and bread she had prepared for
me, wrapped some biscuits in a paper and put them into my bag; then she helped me on with my
10   pelisse* and bonnet, and wrapping herself in a shawl, she and I left the nursery.

    As we passed Mrs. Reed's bedroom she said, "Will you go in and bid Missis good-bye?"

    "No, Bessie: she came to my crib last night when you were gone down to supper, and said I need
not disturb her in the morning, or my cousins either; and she told me to remember that she had always
been my best friend, and to speak of her and be grateful to her accordingly."

15   "What did you say, Miss?"

    "Nothing. I covered my face with the bedclothes, and turned from her to the wall."

    "That was wrong, Miss Jane."

    "It was quite right, Bessie. Your Missis has not been my friend; she has been my foe."

    The moon was set, and it was very dark; Bessie carried a lantern, whose light glanced on wet
20   steps and gravel road sodden by a recent thaw. It wanted but a few minutes of six, and shortly after
that hour had struck, the distant roll of wheels announced the coming coach; I went to the door and
watched its lamps approach rapidly through the gloom.

*pelisse — *winter coat*   **by Charlotte Brontë**

> Answer these questions about the text that you've just read.
> Circle the letter that matches the correct answer.

1.   At what time did Jane get up?

A   Five o'clock
B   Half past four
C   Half past five
D   Four o'clock

(/ 1)

Carry on to the next question → →

2. According to the passage, what did Jane eat for breakfast?

A   Nothing
B   Biscuits
C   Boiled milk and bread
D   Boiled milk

3. According to the passage, how did Jane dress herself?

A   In complete darkness
B   By candlelight
C   By the light of the moon
D   By firelight

4. Why did Jane not go into Mrs Reed's room to say goodbye?

A   Mrs Reed had told her not to.
B   Jane had been unhappy at Gateshead.
C   Jane was in a hurry to leave.
D   It was too early in the morning.

5. Jane said that she had been right to turn her face to the wall when Mrs Reed spoke to her because:

A   she was too angry to talk to her.
B   she did not like Mrs Reed.
C   she didn't want to say something she might regret.
D   Mrs Reed had treated Bessie badly.

6. Which word best describes Bessie?

A   Helpful
B   Excitable
C   Sympathetic
D   Cheerful

7. Which word best describes how Jane feels about her journey?

A   Anxious
B   Eager
C   Agitated
D   Unhappy

8. Which of the following details is not mentioned in the extract?

A   Jane finds it hard to eat when she's about to travel.
B   Jane and Bessie were the only people awake at five o'clock.
C   Mrs Reed is Jane's aunt.
D   Jane was going to leave at six o'clock.

/ 7

9. Which of the following statements is false?

A Jane doesn't have any family.
B Jane hears the coach before she sees it.
C The passage is set during the winter.
D The coach was slightly late.

10. What is the weather like?

A It is raining.
B It was raining, but it has stopped.
C It is snowing.
D It was snowy, but it has melted.

11. What is meant by the word "pressed" (line 8)?

A Suggested
B Encouraged
C Demanded
D Requested

12. What is meant by the word "hardly" (line 1)?

A Only just
B Faintly
C Suddenly
D Gradually

13. What is meant by the word "foe" (line 18)?

A Superior
B Enemy
C Captor
D Rival

14. What is meant by the phrase "It wanted but a few minutes of six" (line 20)?

A It was almost six o'clock.
B It was six minutes past the hour.
C It had just gone six o'clock.
D It was six minutes to the hour.

/ 6

Carry on to the next question → →

Circle the letters which correspond to the correct words to complete the passage below.

Cornwall is a county of

15. **A** exhaustive
B dramatic
C identical
D bland

and contrasting coastlines that can be best

16. **A** contrived
B managed
C explored
D restored

by walking Britain's longest marked footpath, the South West Coast Path. From it you

can experience the breathtaking bays and gently sloping beaches of the south coast,

17. **A** as well as
B in spite of
C even though
D for example

the steep cliffs and sea-lashed rocks of the

18. **A** arduous
B rugged
C neglected
D polluted

north coast. The northern coastline is

19. **A** sprinkles
B sprinkled
C sprinkling
D sprinkle

with resort towns and fishing villages famous for their

20. **A** fragile
B fortuitous
C impetuous
D cobbled

streets and

pastel-hued harbours, which

21. **A** blight
B dot
C disguise
D stifle

the landscape like jewels.

Inland Cornwall also offers plenty for visitors to experience. Follow the steep lanes

22. **A** that
B who
C where
D witch

lead to remote villages where you can enjoy a hearty pub lunch. Look for wildlife

23. **A** during
B among
C despite
D while

dipping your feet

24. **A** out
B with
C besides
D into

the rivers that

25. **A** meander
B erode
C parch
D scamper

through cool, wooded valleys.

Explore the brooding granite heights of Bodmin Moor and bask in the mild climate that

26. **A** suggests
B allows
C complicates
D merges

rare flora and fauna,

27. **A** excluding
B notwithstanding
C including
D counting

the famous Cornish heath, to

28. **A** drift
B struggle
C infest
D flourish

29. **A** Lingering
B Awash
C Corrupted
D Indifferent

with Celtic heritage, Cornwall's landscape contains many signs of its interesting

past. Discover mysterious Bronze Age stone circles and be

30. **A** enchants
B enchanting
C enchanted
D enchant

by Cornwall's rich folklore

— if

31. **A** your
B it's
C they're
D you're

lucky, you might

32. **A** catch
B throw
C spring
D spot

a glimpse of a pixie!

/ 18

Complete the word on the right so that it means the same, or nearly the same, as the word on the left.

Example: rug [c][a][r][p][e][t]

33. extravagant [l][ ][ ][ ][s][h]
34. blade [s][ ][ ][r][d]
35. infamous [n][o][t][o][ ][ ][ ][ ][s]
36. tricky [ ][i][f][f][ ][u][l][ ]
37. unusual [i][r][ ][e][g][u][ ][ ][ ]
38. trip [ ][t][u][m][b][ ][ ]
39. secluded [p][r][i][ ][ ][t][ ]
40. roomy [s][p][a][ ][ ][ ][ ][s]
41. brag [ ][l][o][ ][t]
42. kingdom [r][ ][ ][l][m]
43. detective [ ][l][ ][ ][t][h]
44. sore [t][ ][n][d][ ][ ]

/ 12

Find the word that means the same, or nearly the same, as the word on the left.

Example: **small** <u>tiny</u> strong large soft

45. **stiff** rigid ache brittle bulky

46. **arrogant** vengeful dominant conceited vicious

47. **confused** stunned dubious crestfallen bewildered

48. **watch** review observe inspect vigilant

49. **flinch** wince shroud wrench quiver

50. **start** continue renew resume onset

51. **hurt** puncture eradicate wound obliterate

52. **sleepy** invigorated drowsy drained dormant

53. **unhurried** belated inactive resistant leisurely

54. **old** aged decayed wrinkled gnarled

/ 10

Carry on to the next question → →

Assessment Test 3

> Find the word that means the opposite, or nearly the opposite, of the word on the left.
>
> **Example:**   tame   angry   <u>wild</u>   strong   calm

55. **belief**   lie query question doubt

56. **destroy**   acquire preserve borrow reject

57. **cowardice**   victorious retreat valour swagger

58. **virtuous**   vice corrupt reticent moral

59. **complete**   empty vacant entire partial

60. **dishonest**   sincere secret explain bare

61. **refuse**   suggest enquire accept waste

62. **chaos**   trouble order refined content

63. **lavish**   inexpensive tasteless paltry concealed

64. **culprit**   hostage victim outlaw convict

65. **approve**   dissuade agree comply reject

66. **ordinary**   humble exceptional contemporary imaginative

67. **hostile**   adamant indulgent lenient benevolent

68. **naive**   immature intelligent wily experienced

/ 14

Total   / 68

End of Test

Assessment Test 4

Allow 30 minutes to do this test and work as quickly and as carefully as you can.

You can print **multiple-choice answer sheets** for these questions from our website —
go to www.cgplearning.co.uk/11+. If you'd prefer to answer them in standard write-in
format, just follow the instructions in the question.

> Read this poem carefully and answer the questions that follow.

Adapted from 'The Brook'

By thirty hills I hurry down,
Or slip between the ridges,
By twenty thorpes*, a little town,
And half a hundred bridges.

5   Till last by Philip's farm I flow
To join the brimming river,
For men may come and men may go,
But I go on for ever.

I chatter over stony ways,
10 In little sharps and trebles,
I bubble into eddying bays,
I babble on the pebbles.

I chatter, chatter as I flow
To join the brimming river,
15 For men may come and men may go,
But I go on for ever.

I steal by lawns and grassy plots,
I slide by hazel covers;
I move the sweet forget-me-nots
20 That grow for happy lovers.

I slip, I slide, I gloom, I glance,
Among my skimming swallows;
I make the netted sunbeam dance
Against my sandy shallows.

25 And out again I curve and flow
To join the brimming river,
For men may come and men may go,
But I go on for ever.

by Alfred, Lord Tennyson

*thorpes — *small villages*

> Answer these questions about the text that you've just read.
> Circle the letter of the correct answer.

1.   How many bridges does the brook flow under?

A   One hundred
B   One hundred and fifty
C   Fifty
D   Thirty

2.   What are we told about the brook in verse 2?

A   It flows over stones.
B   It does not pass any buildings.
C   It flows into a different river.
D   Men like to sit and watch it flow by.

/ 2

Carry on to the next question → →

3. Which of the following is not mentioned in the poem?

    A There are fish in the brook.
    B The brook twists and turns.
    C The brook passes by villages.
    D The brook passes by a farm.

4. What sort of land does the brook flow over in verse 3?

    A It is steep and hilly.
    B It is soft and sandy.
    C It is thick with mud.
    D It is covered in stones.

5. What sort of river does the brook flow into?

    A A shallow river with a sandy bed.
    B A river that is almost overflowing.
    C A long and winding river.
    D A fast-flowing river.

6. What kind of weather is mentioned in the poem?

    A Rain
    B Hail
    C Sunshine
    D Wind

7. What does the brook sound like in verse 4?

    A People talking
    B Birds singing
    C People laughing
    D Men walking

8. "For men may come and men may go,
    But I go on for ever" (lines 7-8).
    What do these lines mean?

    A There is a lot of activity around the brook.
    B The brook passes by lots of men because it is so long.
    C The brook will always be there, no matter what happens to the people.
    D There will always be men living near the brook.

/ 6

9. What is meant by the word "skimming" (line 22)?

A To glide across a surface
B To dive into
C To dip into
D To sing sweetly

10. What is meant by the word "babble" (line 12)?

A Wash over
B Grind and scrape
C Drip slowly
D Make noise continuously

/ 2

Fill in the missing letters to complete the words in the following passage.

11. Last night, the **r e s _ d e _ _ s** of Little Hushing were woken once again by strange sounds.

12. The **t _ r r _ _ _ i n g** racket appeared to come from the woods at the edge of the town.

13. The small **_ i l _ _ g _** has now had two weeks of sleepless nights.

14. Mr Beef, the local **_ u _ _ h e r**, said "It sounded like a wild cat".

15. However, his neighbour believes that the **_ o _ _ e** is in fact a bear.

16. Several sightings of the **c r _ _ t _ _ e** have been recorded.

17. Year 5 children saw a long-armed animal **s _ _ i n g _ _ _** through the trees.

18. Joe Jones described seeing a large **_ _ i r y** figure with enormous feet.

19. A group of locals are determined to find the **s _ _ _ c e** of the noise.

20. They are **p _ _ n _ i n g** to trek deep into the woods and set up camp.

21. In the evening, the campers are going to split up and **p _ t _ _ l** the area.

22. Mr Beef is **o _ t _ m _ _ t i _** that they will find whatever is causing the noise.

23. "We have been making **_ r _ p _ r _ t i o n s** all week," he said.

24. "We won't leave the woods until we find this **m _ s t e r _ _ _ s** beast."

25. Let's hope that a hush **_ e _ _ _ n d s** on Little Hushing tonight.

/ 15

Carry on to the next question → →

> Read this passage carefully and answer the questions that follow.

The Voynich Manuscript

The Voynich manuscript is an old and mysterious document. Believed to have been created in the early fifteenth century, the manuscript is written in an unknown language, so nobody knows what it's actually about. The manuscript does contain painted illustrations of plants, which gives a clue to its content. However, most of the species of plants are unknown, which only adds to the manuscript's mystery.

The manuscript is approximately 240 pages long, and the majority of the pages are made from vellum. Vellum is produced by stretching animal skins and was usually reserved for important documents because it was more durable than paper. The text was written using iron gall ink and a quill. The illustrations were coloured using paints, which were probably produced by grinding minerals in a pestle and mortar, and then mixing them with a gum.

A popular theory is that the book is a hoax, because it has peculiar features such as words being repeated two or three times in a row. If countless experts have been unable to determine any meaning from the text, perhaps the manuscript never contained anything meaningful in the first place.

Many historians have tried to trace the book's ownership to prove its origins. Historical documents show that its first confirmed owner was Rudolf II, a Holy Roman Emperor in the late sixteenth century. It eventually ended up in Prague with a man named Georg Baresch. After Baresch, the book was owned by several people before Wilfrid Voynich bought it in 1912. Prior to Voynich, the book was owned by Athanasius Kircher, who had been given it by his friend Jan Marek Marci. Marci had inherited the book after Baresch's death in 1662.

> Answer these questions about the text that you've just read.
> Circle the letter that matches the correct answer.

26. What is the main reason for the Voynich manuscript being 'mysterious'?

A Nobody knows who owned it and when.
B It is written in an unfamiliar language.
C Nobody knows the purpose of the manuscript.
D Nobody knows whether or not it is a fake.

27. Which of these statements cannot be true?

A Athanasius Kircher owned the book after Jan Marek Marci.
B Rudolf II owned the book before Jan Marek Marci.
C Georg Baresch owned the book after Athanasius Kircher.
D Jan Marek Marci owned the book before Wilfrid Voynich.

28. Which of these statements cannot be true?

A Only one copy of the manuscript exists.
B The manuscript took a long time to create.
C The manuscript was created for Rudolf II.
D All other copies of the manuscript have been lost.

29. Which of these statements cannot be true?

A The manuscript contains advice about treating illnesses.
B The manuscript was probably written between 1400 and 1440.
C Voynich was accused of writing the manuscript for financial gain.
D Athanasius Kircher sold the manuscript to Voynich.

/ 4

Complete the word on the right so that it means the same, or nearly the same, as the word on the left.

Example: rug   c a r p e t

30. run   ☐ ☐ ☐ i ☐ t
31. fly   ☐ o ☐ r
32. weak   ☐ e e ☐ ☐ e
33. stroll   d ☐ ☐ d l ☐
34. gruff   h ☐ a r ☐ ☐
35. quick   ☐ a ☐ ☐ d
36. crumple   w ☐ i n ☐ ☐ e
37. emergency   ☐ ☐ i s i ☐
38. stop   c ☐ ☐ s e
39. peel   ☐ ☐ ☐ d

/ 10

Three of the words in each list are linked. Mark the word that is not related to these three.

Example: teacher   doctor   <u>hospital</u>   firefighter

40. hail   snow   sleet   fog

41. upset   bawl   weep   sob

42. sett   burrow   warren   eyrie

43. tongue   bone   gum   tooth

44. candle   torch   beam   lamp

45. leopard   lion   tiger   monkey

46. stable   saddle   rein   stirrup

47. frown   grin   glare   scowl

48. accept   deliver   receive   get

49. lecturer   tutor   assistant   teacher

/ 10

Carry on to the next question → →

Assessment Test 4

In each question below, the words can be rearranged to form a sentence. One word doesn't fit in the sentence. Underline the word that doesn't fit.

Example: mother my <u>head</u> wears pink a hat

50. to it took all me broken weekend it fix

51. is where tonight kennel your dog hiding

52. is favourite least science my best subject

53. think sandwiches crisps said he the for the and thanks

54. dragon wants why to who about read a a story

/ 5

Find the word that means the opposite, or nearly the opposite, of the word on the left.

Example: **tame**   angry <u>wild</u> strong calm

55. **humble**   poor unhappy proud selfish

56. **interesting**   listless mundane obtuse stimulating

57. **reckless**   cautious hasty discreet guarded

58. **plucky**   cowardly diligent lethargic hesitate

59. **functional**   meticulous idle useless futile

60. **fragile**   expendable significant heavy robust

61. **brutal**   gentle vulgar devoted friendly

62. **free**   despondent bound unrestricted captivity

63. **real**   duplicate temporary feigned alternative

64. **clean**   soil disarray unruly drab

65. **replenish**   deplete provisions utilise overstock

66. **bottom**   precipice apex plummet platform

67. **weak**   brash brawny submissive assertive

68. **small**   disproportionate colossal superfluous inordinate

/ 14

Total   / 68

End of Test

Assessment Test 5

Allow 30 minutes to do this test and work as quickly and as carefully as you can.

You can print **multiple-choice answer sheets** for these questions from our website —
go to www.cgplearning.co.uk/11+. If you'd prefer to answer them in standard write-in
format, just follow the instructions in the question.

> Read this passage carefully and answer the questions that follow.

An extract from 'The Crystal Heart'

Mi Nuong's father was an influential Lord. He ruled all of the lands of the Red River, and his
palace stood tall and majestic on its broad, sloping bank. Yet, Mi Nuong was forlorn and melancholy.
Her father kept her locked away at the top of the palace's tallest tower in order to keep her out of harm's
way. Mi Nuong felt trapped; the only company she had was her maid, and her daily routine was always
5   the same. Every day, she would sit by her window embroidering, gazing sorrowfully down at the
waters rushing past far below. Often, she dreamed of being carried away in the fast-flowing rapids to
distant lands.

One morning, Mi Nuong heard music floating through her open window. She hurried over to see
where the sound was coming from. There, on the river below, was a little golden fishing boat. Music
10 rose up from the boat, and Mi Nuong caught snatches of a song: "My love is like a blossom in the
breeze. My love is like a moonbeam on the waves."

The music was captivating, drawing Mi Nuong like a flickering candle flame draws the unwary
moth. The voice was clear and sweet and Mi Nuong leaned out as far as she could to try to catch
sight of the singer. As the boat bobbed past, she glimpsed the tiny figure of a man standing on the
15 prow with a net. A sudden glimmer of hope lit up in her heart and she felt as if she was floating on air.
Perhaps this man had come to release her from the tower. Perhaps he was a Mandarin's son in disguise;
the man she was destined to marry...

> Answer these questions about the text that you've just read.
> Circle the letter that matches the correct answer.

1. Why was Mi Nuong lonely?

A She was confined to the tower.
B She was tired of her daily routine.
C Her maid wasn't very good company.
D She wanted to be rescued by her true love.

2. What does Mi Nuong usually do to pass the time in her tower?

A She sings.
B She dreams of her true love.
C She paints.
D She sews.

/ 2

Carry on to the next question → →

3. What is Mi Nuong's father like?

A   Cruel
B   Proud
C   Protective
D   Arrogant

4. Which one of these things isn't mentioned in the story?

A   Fire
B   Sunlight
C   Moonlight
D   Candlelight

5. How does the music make Mi Nuong feel?

A   Forlorn and lonely
B   Enthralled and wishful
C   Powerful and strong
D   Lovesick and anxious

6. Why is the man on the boat?

A   He hopes to persuade Mi Nuong to marry him.
B   He has come to sing for Mi Nuong's father.
C   He is fishing in the river.
D   He has come to take Mi Nuong to a distant land.

7. Why does Mi Nuong lean as far out of the window as she can?

A   She wants the figure on the fishing boat to see her.
B   She wants to see the singer.
C   She is fascinated by the music.
D   She wants the man on the boat to rescue her.

8. Which of these words best describes how Mi Nuong feels at the end of the passage?

A   Optimistic
B   Relieved
C   Infatuated
D   Besotted

/ 6

9. Which of the following best describes the palace?

A Grand and towering.
B Ornate and magnificent.
C Elevated and garish.
D Splendid and remote.

10. Why is Mi Nuong compared to an "unwary moth" (lines 12-13)?

A She is fragile and delicate.
B She hopes she is going to float away.
C She is mesmerised.
D She is flustered.

11. What is meant by the word "forlorn" (line 2)?

A Distracted
B Miserable
C Disappointed
D Abandoned

12. What is meant by the phrase "she felt as if she was floating on air" (line 15)?

A She felt joyful.
B She couldn't believe what was happening.
C She felt carefree.
D She was in love.

13. What is meant by the phrase "the man she was destined to marry" (line 17)?

A She really wants to marry him.
B She is meant to marry him.
C She is planning to marry him.
D Her father intends her to marry him.

14. What is meant by the phrase "caught snatches" (line 10)?

A Heard several verses
B Recognised parts
C Remembered lyrics
D Heard fragments

/ 6

Carry on to the next question → →

Assessment Test 5

Circle the letters which correspond to the correct words to complete the passage below.

15. **A** broad
    B dramatic
    C narrow daylight when Anne
    D shining

16. **A** awake
    B wakes
    C waked and sat up in bed, staring confusedly
    D awoke

It was

17. **A** moonlight
    B blossom was pouring and outside of which
    C sunshine
    D rain

at the window through which a flood of cheery

18. **A** crept
    B groaned
    C waved across glimpses of blue sky.
    D collected

something white and feathery

19. **A** accept
    B remember where she was. First came a delightful thrill, as
    C endure
    D suspect

For a moment she could not

20. **A** was
    B were
    C are Green Gables and they didn't
    D is

something very pleasant; then a horrible remembrance. This

21. **A** however
    B although she wasn't a boy!
    C so
    D because

want her

22. **A** inside
    B outside of her window. With
    C under
    D beneath

But it was morning and, yes, it was a cherry-tree in full bloom

23. **A** below
    B up
    C across the floor. She pushed up the sash — it went up stiffly
    D through

a bound she was out of bed and

24. **A** who
    B whose was the case; and it stuck so tight
    C which
    D that

and creakily, as if it hadn't been opened for a long time,

25. **A** nothing
    B everything was needed to hold it up.
    C someone
    D something

that

26. **A** glared
    B gazed out into the June morning, her eyes glistening with
    C leapt
    D frowned

Anne dropped on her knees and

27. **A** Because
    B Fortunately she wasn't really going to
    C Hopefully
    D Suppose

delight. Oh, wasn't it beautiful? Wasn't it a lovely place?

28. **A** she
    B it
    C who was. There was scope for imagination here.
    D I

stay here! She would imagine

29. **A** bark
    B roots
    C leaf tapped against the house, and it
    D boughs

A huge cherry-tree grew outside, so close that its

30. **A** totally
    B completely a leaf was to be seen.
    C nearly
    D hardly

was so thick-set with blossoms that

/ 16

From 'Anne of Green Gables' by L.M. Montgomery

Fill in the missing letters to complete the words in the following passage.

31. Last Friday, skateboarders staged a [p][r][ ][t][ ][ ][ ] against developers' plans to close a local skate park.

32. People [g][a][ ][ ][ ][ ][r][e][d] by the council's offices to give a petition to the mayor.

33. The mayor's support for the closure has caused [ ][ ][r][y] amongst locals.

34. "It's the only place we've got to [ ][r][a][c][ ][ ][ ][e]," said one young protester.

35. "It's [ ][ ][d][i][c][u][l][ ][ ][s] that they want to close the park," said another.

36. A number of [ ][l][d][ ][r][ ][y] residents support the skateboarders' cause.

37. "These [ ][o][ ][n][ ][s][t][ ][r][s] need somewhere to skate," said Elsie Smith.

38. "They've got [ ][ ][w][ ][e][r][ ] else and it stops them from using the road."

39. The skate park was given a 'face lift' last May with money [ ][a][i][ ][e][ ] by locals.

40. The new park [ ][n][c][ ][ ][ ][e][s] half pipes, mini ramps and flat bars.   (/ 10)

Find the word that means the same, or nearly the same, as the word on the left.

Example: **small**   <u>tiny</u>   strong   large   soft

41. **hidden**   astray   evade   inconspicuous   addled

42. **float**   levitate   launch   swoop   skim

43. **glum**   dejected   coy   brusque   surly

44. **peaceful**   tranquil   divine   motionless   stagnant

45. **quiet**   boisterous   subdued   abashed   hesitant

46. **unimportant**   futile   unproductive   trivial   pessimistic

47. **explosive**   rowdy   volatile   unruly   hazardous

48. **spiral**   domed   twirled   flourish   helix

49. **crafty**   disloyal   devious   faithless   cheating

50. **consider**   decree   interrogate   deliberate   ultimate

(/ 10)

Carry on to the next question → →

Assessment Test 5

Find the word that means the opposite, or nearly the opposite, of the word on the left.

Example: **tame**   angry <u>wild</u> strong calm

51. **tasty**   peppery pungent saccharine unpalatable

52. **unknown**   obvious celebrated visible noticeable

53. **after**   original preceding native primitive

54. **early**   remiss postpone tardy cancel

55. **alert**   bewildered reluctant wary lethargic

56. **bald**   shaggy mottled wiry fibrous

57. **content**   determined zealous pessimistic dissatisfied

58. **extend**   compile contract summarise embody

59. **still**   placid statuesque turbulent lithe

60. **plain**   intense cumbersome austere garish

61. **flawed**   impeccable amended enhanced adequate

62. **neat**   threadbare faded lacklustre dishevelled

63. **exciting**   verbose banal conventional demanding

64. **strengthen**   debilitate implicate restrict dodder

/ 14

In each question below, the words can be rearranged to form a sentence. One word doesn't fit in the sentence. Underline that word that doesn't fit.

Example: mother my <u>head</u> wears pink a hat

65. ours party the details the of need I

66. in to dark is the dangerous from play it

67. too during the time sun went holidays quickly

68. would about his likes Pete past to songs write

/ 4

Total   / 68

End of Test

Assessment Test 6

Allow 30 minutes to do this test and work as quickly and as carefully as you can.

You can print **multiple-choice answer sheets** for these questions from our website —
go to www.cgplearning.co.uk/11+. If you'd prefer to answer them in standard write-in
format, just follow the instructions in the question.

Read this passage carefully and answer the questions that follow.

If You Go Down to the Woods Today

Arguments continue to rage as to whether big cats such as panthers, pumas, leopards and lynx
are stalking the British countryside. Hundreds, if not thousands, of anxious members of the public
have reported sightings of these creatures, and stories of unexplained attacks on livestock continue to
appear in local newspapers. Reported sightings come from all over the United Kingdom, but some
5 areas produce more reports of mysterious creatures than others, leading to local legends such as
Cornwall's famous Beast of Bodmin.

For many, these large felines living in our midst are no more than rural myths and the reports
are dismissed as hoaxes, mistakes or fantasies. However, not everybody rejects the idea that these
big cats might be living wild in remote parts of our countryside. An increasing number of people
10 believe that there are too many witnesses for the rumours to be unfounded. They also point out that
several sightings and reports of attacks on livestock originate from farmers: people who may not
know much about big cats but who do know the countryside well.

There are various theories about how these exotic creatures may have come to be resident in
our countryside. Some believe that the animals might have escaped from zoos or wildlife parks.
15 Another explanation is that owners abandoned the wild animals when they became too large to
handle, or released them when the Dangerous Wild Animals Act was introduced in the 1970s. It's
possible that these owners travelled to remote areas of the country where they released animals that
they were no longer permitted to keep.

Answer these questions about the text that you've just read.
Circle the letter that matches the correct answer.

1. Which of the following is given as evidence for the existence of big cats in the wild?

A Anxious people
B Newspaper reports
C Attacks on animals
D Rumours

2. How do people who have reported sightings feel about the possibility of wild cats living in Britain?

A Enraged
B Concerned
C Sceptical
D Indecisive

/ 2

Carry on to the next question → →

3. Which of the following is not given as a possible reason for the reported sightings?

A The sightings are real.
B The sightings are dreams.
C The sightings are errors.
D The sightings are lies.

4. What reason is given for the growing number of people who believe the reports?

A The reports have been published in local newspapers, so more people have read them.
B The number of attacks on livestock has increased.
C Several big cats have escaped from zoos, so they must be living in the wild.
D There are many reports, so people think they can't all be false.

5. According to the passage, which of the following statements is true?

A The attacks on livestock made national news.
B No reports have come from Scotland.
C The Beast of Bodmin is a wild cat.
D Many sightings have come from Cornwall.

6. According to the passage, what are the farmers' reports like?

A Trustworthy, because they are familiar with the land.
B Reliable, because they live in remote places.
C Mistaken, because they spread rumours.
D Unreliable, because they don't know much about big cats.

7. Why might owners have released big cats after the Dangerous Wild Animals Act was introduced?

A Their animals were too dangerous to keep.
B The Act allowed the big cats to live only in remote areas.
C Keeping big cats became illegal.
D The animals grew too big to be kept indoors.

8. Why do you think the writer says that "Arguments continue to rage" (line 1)?

A Nobody can agree what kind of animal they have seen.
B People feel strongly about the issue.
C Farmers are angry about losing livestock.
D Most people argue that wild cats exist.

/ 6

9.   Why do you think owners released their pets in remote areas?

A   They were embarrassed.
B   They wanted them to breed in the wild.
C   They didn't want anyone else to take in their pets.
D   They thought there would be less chance of attacks on people.

10. Which of the following best describes big cats?

A   Foreign and misunderstood
B   Elusive and domesticated
C   Foreign and elusive
D   Aggressive and misunderstood

11. What is meant by the word "rural" (line 7)?

A   Suburban
B   Rustic
C   Uncommon
D   Wild

12. What is meant by the word "mysterious" (line 5)?

A   Concealed
B   Impossible
C   Inexplicable
D   Fabricated

13. What is meant by the phrase "living in our midst" (line 7)?

A   Hiding in the shadows
B   Residing amongst us
C   Surviving on our land
D   Existing only in stories

14. Which word best describes this type of article?

A   Biased
B   Factual
C   Mythical
D   Judgemental

/ 6

Carry on to the next question → →

Circle the letters which correspond to the correct words to complete the passage below.

On the 5th December 1872, while

15. **A** sail
B sailed
C sailing
D sails

in the Atlantic Ocean, the helmsman of the

Dei Gratia caught sight of another ship on the horizon. Almost

16. **A** frequently
B immediately
C always
D definitely

, he knew that

something was

17. **A** faulty
B missing
C misleading
D amiss

. Through his telescope, he could see that the ship's sails were

tattered and that she was

18. **A** drifting
B sinking
C disappearing
D deteriorating

aimlessly. The crew were ordered to chase down the

mysterious ship to ensure that her captain wasn't in distress.

19. **A** While
B As
C Although
D Since

they neared the vessel,

they

20. **A** discussed
B doubted
C denied
D realised

that the ship was in fact the *Mary Celeste*, a ship that had

21. **A** started
B put
C set
D opened

sail from

the same harbour, and at

22. **A** near
B after
C before
D around

the same time as the *Dei Gratia*. The *Dei Gratia*'s chief mate

23. **A** swam
B mounted
C dived
D clambered

aboard and began to call out. His shouts received

24. **A** lots of
B some
C no
D few

reply, and it soon

became

25. **A** likely
B possible
C apparent
D doubtful

that there was no one else aboard. At first, he thought that perhaps the crew

had been the unfortunate victims of piracy,

26. **A** because
B since
C but
D when

all the crew's belongings were still on board,

there was no sign of a violent struggle and her

27. **A** valuable
B incomplete
C suitable
D worthless

cargo — barrels of expensive alcohol —

was untouched. The more he

28. **A** foresaw
B investigated
C guessed
D suspected

, the more he began to

29. **A** know
B realise
C wonder
D assume

whether the crew

had vanished

30. **A** to
B in
C into
D through

thin air.

31. **A** In
B To
C For
D Before

this day, what happened to the crew of the *Mary Celeste*

32. **A** stays
B realises
C remains
D implies

a mystery.

/ 18

Complete the word on the right so that it means the opposite, or nearly the opposite, of the word on the left.

Example: smooth   r o u g h

33. noisy   h ☐ s h ☐ ☐

34. fat   b ☐ ☐ y

35. inactive   ☐ n e r ☐ ☐ ☐ i c

36. dull   ☐ l o ☐ s y

37. easy   ☐ r d ☐ o ☐ s

38. real   b o ☐ u ☐

39. bold   ☐ e m u r ☐

40. unfriendly   a f ☐ a b ☐ ☐

41. cheerful   ☐ t e ☐ n

42. irritating   ☐ o o ☐ ☐ i n ☐

43. shiny   ☐ a t ☐ e

44. gather   ☐ i ☐ ☐ r ☐ b u t e

/ 12

Mark the word outside the brackets that has a similar meaning to the words in both sets of brackets.

Example: (find discover) (stain blemish)   freckle smudge <u>spot</u> see

45. (gift donation)   (introduce display)   favour show present prize

46. (motive aim)   (consider think)   intention reason imagine end

47. (grab seize)   (snag obstacle)   catch problem difficulty clutch

48. (canyon chasm)   (devour binge)   abyss ravine gorge guzzle

49. (guide control)   (straightforward honest)   direct aim open steer

50. (crop produce)   (submit surrender)   supply yield succumb comply

51. (selfish miserly)   (middle medium)   greedy average mean stingy

52. (filling load)   (fulfilled happy)   comfortable stuffing packing content

53. (item article)   (disagree contest)   object entity challenge oppose

54. (gaunt haggard)   (sketched doodled)   drawn wasted painted worn

/ 10

Carry on to the next question → →

Assessment Test 6

> Find the word that means the same, or nearly the same, as the word on the left.
>
> **Example:** small <u>tiny</u> strong large soft

55. **sociable**   maternal gregarious gleeful whimsical

56. **worried**   aghast composed cautious apprehensive

57. **cut**   sabotage shatter incision jagged

58. **wild**   tempestuous spiteful prohibited corrupt

59. **colour**   vibrant pigment veneer mauve

60. **even**   authentic honourable uniform reciprocal

61. **mercy**   poise composure lavish clemency

62. **extra**   superfluous wasteful plentiful extravagant

63. **criticise**   inferior extol belittle sullen

64. **unusual**   conventional unorthodox fascinating enticing

65. **unstable**   substantial precarious disintegrate decrepit

66. **queasy**   feverish nauseous frail venerable

67. **friend**   amity confidant colleague neighbour

68. **question**   debrief retort perceptive accomplish

/ 14

Total   / 68

End of Test

Assessment Test 7

Allow 30 minutes to do this test and work as quickly and as carefully as you can.

You can print **multiple-choice answer sheets** for these questions from our website — go to www.cgplearning.co.uk/11+. If you'd prefer to answer them in standard write-in format, just follow the instructions in the question.

> Read this poem carefully and answer the questions that follow.

The Way Through the Woods

They shut the road through the woods
Seventy years ago.
Weather and rain have undone it again,
And now you would never know
5 There was once a road through the woods
Before they planted the trees.
It is underneath the coppice and heath,
And the thin anemones.
Only the keeper sees
10 That, where the ring-dove broods,
And the badgers roll at ease,
There was once a road through the woods.

Yet, if you enter the woods
Of a summer evening late,
15 When the night-air cools on the trout-ringed pools
Where the otter whistles his mate.
(They fear not men in the woods
Because they see so few),
You will hear the beat of a horse's feet
20 And the swish of a skirt in the dew,
Steadily cantering through
The misty solitudes,
As though they perfectly knew
The old lost road through the woods...
25 But there is no road through the woods.

by Rudyard Kipling

> Answer these questions about the text that you've just read.
> Circle the letter that matches the correct answer.

1. Which of the following statements about the road is false?
There is no road through the woods because:

A the rain has eroded it.
B trees have been planted over it.
C horses have worn it away.
D it has become overgrown.

2. Which of these is not mentioned in the poem?

A When they shut the road.
B What the woods are like.
C The sounds in the wood.
D What the road was like.

/ 2

Carry on to the next question → →

3. What do lines 7-12 focus on?

A Who shut the road.
B How the poet feels about the woods.
C What the woods used to be like.
D What the woods are like now.

4. Which word best describes what the animals in the woods are like?

A Afraid
B Endangered
C Solitary
D Carefree

5. Which adjective best describes the poet's tone in lines 1-2?

A Pleased
B Matter-of-fact
C Confused
D Frustrated

6. The poet describes "trout-ringed pools" (line 15). What do you think they are?

A Pools of water where the otters drink
B Pools of water surrounded by trees
C Perfectly round pools of water
D Pools where fish are rippling the water's surface

7. How do the otters feel about men?

A Intimidated
B Indifferent
C Fearful
D Positive

8. What is happening in lines 19-24?

A The poet is hunting animals in the woods.
B The poet is imagining that other people are in the woods.
C The poet is talking to other people in the woods.
D The poet is dancing on the road.

/ 6

9. Which of the following statements is true?

A The keeper wants to keep the road a secret.
B Only men used the road.
C People used to ride along the road.
D The road was closed because too few people used it

10. What is meant by the word "coppice" (line 7)?

A An abandoned building
B Small trees and shrubs
C Wild flowers
D A small lake

11. What is meant by the word "broods" (line 10)?

A Sleeps
B Builds nests
C Sings
D Hatches eggs

12. What is meant by the phrase "a summer evening late" (line 14)?

A An evening at the start of autumn.
B An evening at the end of summer.
C Nearly nightfall on a summer's day.
D An unusually warm evening.

13. What is meant by the word "solitudes" (line 22)?

A Dark places
B Lonely places
C Beautiful places
D Wild places

14. What is meant by the phrase "They fear not men" (line 17)?

A They attack humans.
B They aren't afraid of people.
C They don't frighten people.
D They are tame.

/ 6

Carry on to the next question → →

Assessment Test 7

> Circle the letters which correspond to the correct words to complete the passage below.

The Hope Diamond is one of the most

15. **A** neglected
B remarkable
C challenging
D burnished

precious stones in the world. It isn't

the largest diamond ever recorded,

16. **A** nor
B either
C or
D since

is it the most valuable, but it does have a

17. **A** mediocre
B reticent
C tedious
D fascinating

history. The Hope Diamond was

18. **A** never
B temporarily
C mainly
D originally

part of a larger diamond

called the Tavernier Blue. The Tavernier Blue, named

19. **A** in spite of
B considering its deep blue colour,
C because of
D regarding

was first bought by a man called Jean-Baptiste Tavernier in the 17th century. Tavernier sold the

diamond

20. **A** to
B with
C for
D of

King Louis XIV of France, and it became part of the French Crown Jewels.

In the late 18th century, the French monarchy

21. **A** were
B is
C are
D was

overthrown. The diamond was stolen

and

22. **A** definitely
B seemingly
C substantially
D scarcely

vanished for several decades. The diamond

23. **A** habitually
B never
C probably
D eventually

reappeared

in London, and passed

24. **A** by
B through
C into
D via

several different owners, including Henry Phillip Hope, for

25. **A** what
B who
C which
D whom

the jewel is named. In 1949, the jeweller Harry Winston

26. **A** purchased
B destroyed
C mislaid
D brought

the Hope

Diamond. Winston

27. **A** donated
B owed
C borrowed
D advertised

the Hope Diamond to the Smithsonian Natural History museum,

28. **A** where
B when
C there
D while

it is currently on display. It's thought that the Hope Diamond, worth about $250 million,

is one of the most

29. **A** inexpensive
B controversial
C visited
D insipid

museum exhibits in the world, with an

30. **A** assumed
B apparent
C imagined
D estimated

100 million people believed to have viewed the gem.

/ 16

Complete the word on the right so that it means the opposite, or nearly the opposite, of the word on the left.

Example: smooth ⬚r⬚o⬚u⬚g⬚h⬚

31. plentiful   ⬚_⬚p⬚_⬚r⬚s⬚_
32. saunter   ⬚h⬚_⬚_⬚t⬚e⬚_
33. knit   ⬚_⬚n⬚_⬚_⬚v⬚_⬚l
34. graceful   ⬚_⬚w⬚_⬚_⬚a⬚r⬚d
35. calm   ⬚u⬚_⬚r⬚u⬚_⬚_
36. extravagant   ⬚_⬚_⬚u⬚g⬚_⬚l
37. youthful   ⬚_⬚i⬚z⬚_⬚n⬚_⬚_
38. lucky   ⬚h⬚a⬚p⬚_⬚_⬚_⬚s
39. triumph   ⬚t⬚_⬚a⬚_⬚_⬚_⬚y
40. ugly   ⬚c⬚o⬚_⬚_⬚l⬚_

/ 10

Three of the words in each list are linked. Mark the word that is not related to these three.

Example: teacher   doctor   <u>hospital</u>   firefighter

41. free   remain   rescue   release

42. violin   guitar   banjo   mandolin

43. cygnet   tadpole   sow   gosling

44. utter   whisper   mumble   murmur

45. square   triangle   rhombus   rectangle

46. twin   pair   couple   triple

47. gate   fence   wall   railing

48. respond   answer   question   reply

49. race   advance   rush   hurry

50. university   library   college   school

/ 10

Find the word that means the same, or nearly the same, as the word on the left.

Example: **small**   <u>tiny</u>   strong   large   soft

51. **ghost**   haunting   apparition   enchantment   hallucination

52. **faulty**   defective   unsatisfactory   rancid   incorrect

53. **secret**   discreet   covert   restrained   tactful

54. **loyal**   ally   devoted   intuitive   supportive

55. **careful**   observant   orderly   meticulous   immaculate

56. **danger**   catastrophe   outrage   treachery   peril

57. **clumsy**   vicarious   sluggish   awkward   dexterous

58. **annoy**   exasperate   irate   furious   resent

59. **outdo**   succeed   quell   foil   surpass

60. **conflict**   malice   fray   thwart   vanquish

61. **guilt**   sorrow   remorse   anguish   penalty

62. **surly**   loathsome   pensive   temperamental   dour

63. **wise**   solemn   wistful   sage   studious

64. **hopeful**   aspiration   ambitious   intention   optimistic

/ 14

Complete the word on the right so that it means the same, or nearly the same, as the word on the left.

Example: rug   `c` `a` `r` `p` `e` `t`

65. live   `d` `_` `e` `_` `_`

66. tomb   `c` `_` `_` `_` `t`

67. branch   `b` `_` `_` `_` `_`

68. spooky   `_` `_` `r` `_` `e`

/ 4

Total   / 68

End of Test

Assessment Test 8

Allow 30 minutes to do this test and work as quickly and as carefully as you can.

You can print **multiple-choice answer sheets** for these questions from our website — go to www.cgplearning.co.uk/11+. If you'd prefer to answer them in standard write-in format, just follow the instructions in the question.

> Read this poem carefully and answer the questions that follow.

The Tiger

Tiger, tiger, burning bright
In the forests of the night,
What immortal hand or eye
Could frame thy fearful symmetry?

5 In what distant deeps or skies
Burnt the fire of thine eyes?
On what wings dare he aspire?
What the hand dare seize the fire?

And what shoulder and what art,
10 Could twist the sinews of thy heart?
And, when thy heart began to beat,
What dread hand and what dread feet?

What the hammer? what the chain?
In what furnace was thy brain?
15 What the anvil? what dread grasp
Dare its deadly terrors clasp?

When the stars threw down their spears,
And watered heaven with their tears,
Did He smile His work to see?
20 Did He who made the lamb make thee?

Tiger, tiger, burning bright
In the forests of the night,
What immortal hand or eye
Dare frame thy fearful symmetry?

by William Blake

> Answer these questions about the text that you've just read.
> Circle the letter that matches the correct answer.

1. Which of these statements best describes how the poet feels about the tiger?

A The poet is jealous of the tiger.
B The poet loves the tiger.
C The poet hates the tiger.
D The poet is afraid of the tiger.

2. Which of the following does the poet not ask about?

A Where the tiger was made
B How the tiger was made
C When the tiger was made
D What was used to make the tiger

/ 2

Carry on to the next question → →

3. What do lines 23-24 suggest about the tiger's creator?

A He is uncertain about the tiger.
B He is brave to have made the tiger.
C He is proud of the tiger.
D He regrets creating the tiger.

4. Why are the "hammer", "chain", "furnace" and "anvil" mentioned in verse 4?

A These tools were needed to make the tiger.
B The poet compares making a tiger to the work of a blacksmith.
C They are weapons full of "deadly terrors".
D The poet is comparing the tiger's paws to weapons.

5. "Did He smile His work to see?" (line 19).
    This question is asking:

A How the tiger felt after being created.
B Whether the stars were happy when the tiger was made.
C How the tiger's creator felt after making the animal.
D Why the tiger's creator is happy.

6. "Did He who made the lamb make thee?" (line 20).
    This question is asking:

A Why the creator made both a lamb and a tiger.
B If the lamb was made before the tiger.
C If the tiger and the lamb are actually so different.
D If the same creator made the tiger and the lamb.

7. Who do you think the poet is addressing in the poem?

A The lamb
B The tiger
C The tiger's creator
D The reader

8. Why do you think the poem is made up of unanswered questions?

A The tiger's creator refuses to answer the poet.
B The tiger cannot answer the poet.
C The tiger's creator is now in heaven.
D The creation of the tiger is beyond human understanding.

/ 6

9. What is meant by the word "immortal" (line 3)?

A Enduring
B Transitory
C Powerful
D Evolving

10. What is meant by the word "twist" (line 10)?

A Wind
B Make
C Reverse
D Unravel

/ 2

> Fill in the missing letters to complete the words in the following passage.

11. Cheese comes in hundreds of different tastes and ☐☐ x t ☐ r e s,

12. from strong blue cheeses like Roquefort, to ☐☐ l d ☐ r soft cheeses like Brie.

13. Turning milk into cheese is a ☐☐☐ f t that predates written records.

14. Making cheese was originally a way of ☐ r e s ☐☐☐ i n g milk.

15. Nowadays, people buy cheese for its taste and ☐ e r s ☐☐ i l i t y.

16. Modern technology means that cheese can be produced on a much larger ☐☐☐ l e,

17. and cheeses that were traditionally produced in a particular ☐ e ☐☐ o n

can now be made all over the world.

18. However, some cheese makers ☐ o n ☐ i n ☐ e to make their cheese by hand,

19. which can be a ☐ e n ☐☐☐ y process. Hand-made cheeses are often made

20. using traditional ☐ e t ☐ o ☐☐. These are less precise than using machines,

21. so it can be challenging to make each batch ☐☐ n s i ☐ t ☐ n t.

22. Cheese connoisseurs claim that hand-made cheeses taste ☐ u ☐ e r ☐☐ r to

23. factory-made cheeses, and some artisan cheeses can c ☐☐☐☐ n d high prices.

24. One of world's most ☐☐☐ e n s i ☐ e hand-made cheeses is made using donkey

25. milk — a kilogram of this cheese can f ☐☐☐ h up to £875.

/ 15

Carry on to the next question → →

Assessment Test 8

Read the passage carefully and answer the questions that follow.

Laika — The Rocket Dog

Laika was the first animal to orbit the Earth. Her journey into space was an important victory for the Soviet Union in the Space Race between themselves and the United States of America. The Space Race was a way of proving to the world, and to each other, who was the more advanced nation. It had begun in 1957 with Sputnik 1, the world's first satellite, and it ended in 1975 with a joint mission between the two superpowers. Between these dates the world also witnessed the first spacecraft to impact the moon (in 1959), the first man in space and the first man on the moon.

Laika was a stray mongrel found on the streets of Moscow. She received intensive training, along with two other Moscow strays, before being chosen to orbit the Earth inside Sputnik 2. The Soviet Union realised that sending an animal into space was an important step in their ultimate goal of sending a human into space. Nobody knew how going into space would affect a living organism and they wanted to test how Laika would withstand weightlessness and the intense rocket launch.

Even before Laika went into space she was popular with the scientists who worked with her, as well as with the world's media. She was a docile dog, who did not fight with the other dogs she trained with. Out of the three dogs, Laika performed the best in training.

In an attempt to beat the US to being the first nation to send a living creature into space, the Soviets rushed the construction of Sputnik 2, meaning that the satellite was not fully tested. The technology to bring a spacecraft back to earth intact had not been perfected when the vessel was launched, so the journey of Sputnik 2 was always going to be a one-way trip.

The Soviets claimed that they were going to put Laika down with a batch of poisoned food, but following the mission there were reports of Laika dying from a lack of oxygen. It was only in 2002, 45 years after the launch of Sputnik 2, that it was made public that Laika had died a few hours into the flight due to overheating. It was claimed that because of a problem during launch, the temperature control system didn't function correctly. This meant that temperatures reached dangerous levels in a relatively short space of time.

When Laika was launched into space, animal rights groups around the world claimed it was wrong to harm animals to aid human advancement. In the Soviet Union, however, the decision to send a dog to its death wasn't questioned until over forty years later. It was only in 1998 that the Russian scientist Oleg Gazenko came forward to express regret about what they had done. He said that they shouldn't have done it and that they "did not learn enough from this mission to justify the death of the dog."

Laika wasn't the last dog to be sent into space, but all future space missions involving dogs were designed to return safely to earth.

Answer these questions about the text that you've just read.
Circle the letter that matches the correct answer.

26. Which of these statements must be true?

A   The USA was considered a superpower in the 1970s.
B   Laika was the last dog to die in a space mission.
C   Sputnik 2 was only in orbit for a few hours.
D   The Soviets won the Space Race.

27. What was the main reason that Laika was chosen to go into space?

A   She was a docile dog.
B   She was popular with the media and the scientists.
C   She excelled in the training exercises.
D   She was a stray dog.

28. Which of these statements cannot be true?

A   The Space Race took place over a period of 18 years.
B   The first satellite to impact the moon occurred before Sputnik 2.
C   The US wasn't interested in sending a dog into space.
D   The Soviets lied about Laika's death.

29. Why do you think the Soviet Union didn't publicly question the decision
    to send Laika to her death until 1998?

A   Because what they learnt from Laika's death helped to save the lives of human astronauts.
B   Because they didn't know how Laika had died.
C   Because they didn't want to undermine one of their greatest victories.
D   Because they weren't interested in animal rights.

/ 4

Carry on to the next question → →

Assessment Test 8

Find the word that means the same, or nearly the same, as the word on the left.

Example: **small** <u>tiny</u> strong large soft

30. **disrespectful** insolent reckless negligent shameful

31. **shrill** harmonious piercing sonorous booming

32. **charming** sophisticated dignified genteel suave

33. **hard-working** diligent lethargic competent proficient

34. **ugly** withered grotesque disgraceful unpleasant

35. **vain** haughty overbearing conceited flamboyant

36. **lucky** prosperous thriving fortuitous abundance

37. **obedient** content vicarious mellow submissive

/ 8

Complete the word on the right so that it means the same, or nearly the same, as the word on the left.

Example: rug [c][a][r][p][e][t]

38. wander [r][ ][a][ ]

39. fight [ ][ ][ ][s][ ][l][e]

40. unfriendly [ ][l][ ][ ][f]

41. taupe [b][ ][ ][ ][e]

42. hurdle [ ][ ][s][ ][a][c][ ][e]

43. location [v][ ][n][ ][ ]

44. new [ ][e][ ][ ][ ][t]

45. poison [ ][e][ ][m]

46. fame [ ][ ][o][r][ ]

47. warn [ ][ ][ ][t][ ][o][n]

48. line [c][o][l][ ][ ][ ]

49. disaster [f][ ][ ][s][ ][o]

/ 12

Find the word that means the opposite, or nearly the opposite, of the word on the left.

Example: tame   angry <u>wild</u> strong calm

50. **sympathetic**   fastidious callous uncouth surly

51. **long-winded**   deficient incomplete senseless pithy

52. **modest**   introverted courageous egotistical sanguine

53. **coy**   conspicuous blatant overwhelming solitary

54. **simple**   intricate linear orthodox comprehensive

55. **polite**   timid discourteous candid scrupulous

56. **active**   fatigued dormant weary tiresome

57. **generous**   avaricious imprudent cordial malicious

58. **allow**   disagree veto restrict impassable

59. **unfussy**   ravenous vicarious fastidious circumspect

60. **unclear**   formidable manifest sequestered strenuous

61. **strict**   tactful lenient considerate chivalrous

62. **careless**   inquisitive abrupt scrupulous stringent

63. **patient**   agitated intolerant disturbed belligerent

/ 14

In each question below, the words can be rearranged to form a sentence. One word doesn't fit in the sentence. Underline that word that doesn't fit.

Example: mother my <u>head</u> wears pink a hat

64. to it hates cook likes but Cho pasta so eating

65. am that is but slight worse I says she she awful

66. to checked suitcase Japan trip booked we the we our before forecast

67. run because I I clocks always early set my late soon

68. who to used by lived we the outside know someone sea

/ 5

Total   / 68

End of Test

Assessment Test 8

Glossary

adjective	A word that <u>describes</u> a <u>noun</u>, e.g. '<u>beautiful</u> morning', '<u>frosty</u> lawn'.
adverb	A word that <u>describes</u> a <u>verb</u>, which often ends with the <u>suffix</u> '<u>-ly</u>', e.g. 'She laughed <u>happily</u>.', 'He ran <u>quickly</u>.'
antonym	A word that has the <u>opposite meaning</u> to another word, e.g. the antonym of 'good' is 'bad'.
connective	A word that <u>joins</u> two clauses or sentences, e.g. '<u>and</u>', '<u>but</u>', '<u>therefore</u>'.
consonants	The <u>21 letters</u> of the alphabet that <u>aren't vowels</u>.
fiction	Text that has been <u>made up</u> by the author, about <u>imaginary people</u> and <u>events</u>.
homographs	Words that are spelt the same but have <u>different meanings</u>, e.g. 'I want to <u>play</u>.' and 'I saw a <u>play</u>.'
homophones	Words that <u>sound the same</u>, but mean different things, e.g. '<u>hair</u>' and '<u>hare</u>'.
imagery	Language that creates a <u>vivid picture</u> in the reader's mind.
metaphor	A way of <u>describing</u> something by saying that it <u>is</u> something else, e.g. 'John's legs were lead weights.'
multiple choice	A type of <u>11+ question</u> that gives you <u>answers</u> to choose from.
non-fiction	Text that is about <u>facts</u> and <u>real people</u> and <u>events</u>.
noun	A word that <u>names</u> something, e.g. '<u>Paul</u>', '<u>cat</u>', '<u>fear</u>', '<u>childhood</u>'.
personification	A way of describing something by giving it <u>human feelings</u> and <u>characteristics</u>, e.g. 'The cruel wind plucked remorselessly at my threadbare clothes.'
prefix	A string of letters that can be put <u>in front</u> of a word to <u>change its meaning</u>, e.g. '<u>un-</u>' can be added to '<u>lock</u>' to make '<u>unlock</u>'.
pronoun	Words that can be used <u>instead</u> of <u>nouns</u>, e.g. '<u>I</u>', '<u>you</u>', '<u>he</u>', '<u>it</u>'.
simile	A way of describing something by <u>comparing</u> it to something else, e.g. 'The stars were <u>like</u> a thousand diamonds, glittering in the sky.'
subject	The <u>person</u> or <u>thing</u> <u>doing</u> the action of a verb, e.g. '<u>Jo</u> laughed.', '<u>The bird</u> flew.'
suffix	A string of letters that can be put <u>after</u> a word to <u>change its meaning</u>, e.g. '<u>-er</u>' can be added to the end of '<u>play</u>' to make '<u>player</u>'.
synonym	A word with a <u>similar meaning</u> to another word, e.g. '<u>big</u>' is a synonym of '<u>huge</u>'.
verb	An <u>action</u> or <u>doing</u> word, e.g. '<u>run</u>', '<u>went</u>', '<u>think</u>', or a <u>being</u> word, e.g. '<u>is</u>'.
vowels	The letters '<u>a</u>', '<u>e</u>', '<u>i</u>', '<u>o</u>' and '<u>u</u>'.